CONTENTS

Trails

THE TRAILS

ACKNOWLEDGEMENTS

The 'Let's Go! Science Trails' and 'Let's Go! STEM Trails' projects have been a success due to the commitment and enthusiasm of all the schools involved.

A big 'thank you' should go to:
All the children and staff at the following schools, who contributed to the development of Trails in these books:

Haringey Schools with Dan Hawkins:
Alexandra Primary School
Campsbourne Primary School
Crowland Primary School
Ferry Lane Primary School
Muswell Hill Primary School
Stroud Green Primary School
Tiverton Primary School
The Green CE Primary School
Welbourne Primary School
Weston Park Primary School

Dorset Schools with Katrina Halford:
St Andrews CE VC Primary School
Sherborne Primary School
Abbey CE Primary School
Thornford CE VA Primary School
All Saints CE Primary School
Buckland Newton CE Primary School
Trent Young's Endowed CE Primary School

Chichester Schools:
Rumboldswhyke C of E Infants School
Central CE Junior School
Kingsham Primary School
Birdham CE Primary School
St Richards RC Primary School
Parklands Primary School
Fishbourne CE Primary School
Portfield Primary School
Lavant CE Primary School
Singleton CE Primary School

PSTT College Fellows who have written Trails or contributed ideas:
Robin James (Exeter Road Community School, Exmouth), Stacey Reid (Latymer All Saints CE Primary School, London), Sarah Eames (Sandfield Close Primary School, Leicester), Caroline Skerry (St Joseph's School, Launceston) and Nicky Collins (Yealmpton Primary School, Plymouth).

June Isik and Natasha Serret for inspiration from their own work and for initial project ideas and, in addition, to June Isik for designing the original project logos.

Finally, thanks are due to the Primary Science Teaching Trust for funding and support throughout the development and publication of resources from these projects and to Prof. Dudley Shallcross, Dr. Sophie Franklin, Alison Eley and Sue Martin for all their talents and skills in making this project such a success.

FOREWORD

The Science Trails concept has been expanded from the original book to include technology, engineering and mathematics. The range of Trails is impressive, from algorithms to tessellation, and demonstrates the huge potential of the outdoor classroom. We hope that teachers reading these books will not only have the confidence to use the Trails described within, but will also plan, design and implement their own. We would love to know about new Trails that are devised. This book is the culmination of inputs from many outstanding teachers and we thank them all. However, PSTT Fellows Jeannette Morgan and Dan Hawkins deserve special mention for proposing the original idea and we are delighted to see the outcome of their vision.

Professor Dudley E. Shallcross
CEO of the Primary Science Teaching Trust

INTRODUCTION

INTRODUCTION

When you go outside, two things should immediately be apparent: the magnificence of the natural world and the achievements of human innovation. Yet so many incredible things remain unnoticed. The beauty of living things, the laws that govern forces, and the motion that enables us to observe these in action are undoubtedly impressive. Taking time to appreciate this reveals not only natural wonders but also the exceptional ingenuity of the human species. Consider this: everything that has been built, created, constructed or designed started life in someone's imagination. Whether this is a house, a garden, a car, a mobile phone, a pavement, or an automatic sliding door, it all began as an idea. Ideas may be an expression of someone's personality or simply functional, solving a problem. Our world is magnificent and providing opportunity to explore with purpose can enhance the teaching of so many curriculum subjects. This was the premise for writing 'Let's Go! STEM Trails', the follow up book to 'Let's Go! Science Trails'. 'Let's Go! STEM Trails' aims to focus further on opportunities for children to appreciate Science, Technology, Engineering and Maths in the world around them. Using the outdoors, and the Trails specifically, it seeks to encourage children to make links between the STEM subjects, or look at them as discrete subjects and to appreciate their relevance to their everyday lives.

"The best classroom and richest cupboard are roofed only by the sky." – Margaret McMillan c1925

"There are no seven wonders of the world in the eyes of a child. There are seven million." – Walt Streightiff

RATIONALE FOR OUTDOOR LEARNING

The benefits of outdoor learning are very well established and documented. Research has shown that learning about the natural world and built environment will be deeper and more lasting when children are given first hand experience. The amount of time spent outside has been shown to have a positive correlation with general health and well-being as well as with the development of responsible attitudes to the environment (Cotterell and Radik-Cotterell, 2010). In addition, there is evidence that outdoor learning has a positive effect on teacher-child relationships, pupil engagement and attendance (Dillon *et al*, 2005).

Numerous other positive outcomes of learning outside have been demonstrated, for example the development of general life skills, working with others, resilience, self-confidence, risk-taking and risk management. Ofsted (2010) describe how well-planned and implemented outdoor learning experiences make a significant contribution to raising standards and improving pupils' personal, social and emotional development.

The outdoors offers limitless opportunities for children to develop a deeper and more secure understanding of what STEM is, and what scientists, engineers, technologists and designers have achieved in the real world. Children can experience things that they would not inside a classroom. Children's imaginations are sparked by new stimuli and they ask new questions that become meaningful and exciting starting points for all kinds of enquiry. Not convinced? Go and have a look! (Grimshaw *et al*, 2019).

AIMS OF THE 'LET'S GO! STEM TRAILS' PROJECT

- ■ Why go outdoors?
- ■ How can outdoor spaces in the local area enhance learning outcomes for children?
- ■ How can these spaces contribute to teachers' continuing professional development?

These questions were also the premise of the 'Let's Go! Science Trails' project and were successfully answered. So why do it again? 'Let's Go! STEM Trails' aimed to draw on the success of the first project, but widen the scope of subjects covered and look at how the benefits of Trails could be used to enhance children's experiences of other curriculum subjects. This project again drew on a wealth of collective expertise, involving teachers, subject leaders, schools and College Fellows from the Primary Science Teaching Trust.

The main aim of the project was to create an adaptable outdoor learning resource that could be used by teachers in any local environment, anywhere in the world. We wanted the resource to increase teacher confidence in taking children outside as well as aid teachers with curriculum development. The project aimed to shift culture by helping teachers and children to look at the world differently, and to inspire them to think about what else could be created now or in the future. Most importantly, this project raised awareness of what an incredibly rich resource the outdoors is and how, unlike most other resources, it is completely free.

The Trails in this book complement those from the first book, giving new ideas for the areas covered in 'Let's Go! Science Trails'. However, this book also ventures into new areas. There are Trails that cover many aspects of the maths and science curriculum, Trails that cover some aspects of design technology or computing, and Trails that are location-specific and cover all STEM subjects. Many teachers' perceptions of the value of outdoor learning does not extend beyond the biological sciences, particularly the study of habitats or plants. We wanted to create Trails that would support many areas of teaching and learning across a wider spectrum of subjects. Using this approach makes it easier for teachers (and, of course the children) to make links, not only between areas of science, but across all STEM subjects. The Trails are creative and innovative and offer opportunities to make use of appropriate technology to support learning, such as portable computer devices and access to the internet.

All the 'Let's Go! STEM Trails' in this book have been developed, tried and tested, and retried and tested, by groups of teachers across the UK.

USING THE 'LET'S GO! STEM TRAILS'

Each Trail is based on a particular topic or area (e.g. shape), and the location chosen takes the children to see real life examples of this topic or area. Each Trail is theme-specific (e.g. packaging, boats). Children will also focus on how everyday problems have been solved because scientists, engineers, designers and technologists have worked together. Teachers can make adaptations to any Trail so that it can be tailored exactly to the topic or area they want to teach. Where teachers are unsure about taking children to new locations, it is recommended that the first few Trails are carried out in the school grounds. (Morgan *et al*, 2015).

STRUCTURE OF THE TRAILS

Each Trail is organised in the following sections:

AGE RANGE
Suggested age ranges are given for each Trail, but they can be easily adapted as necessary to suit different age ranges.

INTRODUCTION
This section gives an overview of the Trail and the main themes covered.

CONCEPTS EXPLORED IN THE TRAIL
The concepts that are explored in the Trail are described; these have been kept general so that the Trails will work within any particular curriculum.

RESOURCES
A basic set of resources on the Trails could include:
- Digital cameras and/or video cameras
- Maps of locations
- Clipboards
- Writing equipment: whiteboards & pens, paper & pencils

Health and safety resources should include:
- Medical/first aid equipment
- High visibility jackets for safe walking out of school

In addition to these, each Trail specifies any other particular resources you could or may wish to use. A note of caution, however: Trails should require little equipment, so that they do not become too onerous for teachers to organise and/or difficult for children to carry whilst outdoors.

In every instance, it is the responsibility of the teacher/school to carry out an appropriate risk assessment and identify the requisite child:teacher ratios.

PREPARATION
Each Trail has a 'preparation' section. This includes instructions for essential preparatory work as well as suggestions for other preliminary activities that would support the Trail.

INVESTIGATION TYPES
'Let's Go! STEM Trails' provide opportunities for children to engage in different types of exploration and investigation, not just relating to science. Each Trail specifies what investigation types are predominantly being used.

SPECIFIC SKILLS FOCUS
The children will use a range of skills as they carry out the activities on a 'Let's Go! STEM Trail'. Every Trail offers the opportunity for the children to develop, use and apply most of these skills:

observing, listening, predicting, asking questions, collecting and recording data or results, looking for patterns in data, drawing conclusions, answering questions using their own evidence, linking their ideas and explanations to previous knowledge and understanding, making suggestions about further work.

The skills focus section identifies those skills that are particularly relevant to that Trail.

LOCATIONS
Suggested locations are given for each Trail and these should be used as a basis for deciding where to go. Some Trails take place in more than one location so that comparisons can be made between one place and another.

ON THE TRAIL
This section outlines what the children will actually be doing while they are out. It also includes instructions and suggestions for the teacher about how to guide the children through the Trail.

KEY QUESTIONS
Key questions for teachers and supporting adults to use with the children have been suggested.

BACK IN THE CLASSROOM
Follow up activities are given at the end of each Trail. Often these are based on continuing the work done on the actual Trail (e.g. analysing data collected), but also other relevant activities across the curriculum might also be suggested.

PLANNING A NEW TRAIL
The Trails in this book, as well as those in 'Let's Go! Science Trails', could just be a starting point – teachers are encouraged to develop new Trails of their own to suit their own contexts. With so many potential locations, we would encourage teachers to add to this resource. The following guidance might be useful when planning a new Trail.

Trails could be:
■ Child-led
■ Teacher-led
■ Parent-led
■ Topic-led
■ Destination-led
■ Indoor
■ A combination of the above

CHILD-LED
The children choose the location to visit or topic to see in the outdoors. Provided they can justify their choices with good reasons, allowing them to choose can be a valuable way to ensure maximum engagement. It is also an excellent way of assessing how they can apply prior knowledge about an area to decide on the best location.

TEACHER-LED
With most Trails, teachers will choose where to take their children. If preliminary work is required, e.g. advance visits to shops, then this approach is recommended.

PARENT-LED
Parents can be encouraged to take their children on Trails from home. This could be part of a homework task. Many Trails will need extra adults to support, so involving parents makes sense. Having been on Trails with the class, parents might then generate suggestions of their own about where they could take children. They will also benefit from hearing teachers lead discussions with the children, which could improve the quality of discussion they might have at home with their own children.

TOPIC-LED
Some Trails will be generated in order to cover aspects of a particular area of the curriculum. Consideration should be given as to where the children will encounter real-life examples of the topic being studied.

DESTINATION-LED
Where a visit is planned to a particular place, consideration can be given to the possibilities this place offers for learning aspects of STEM subjects. Trails planned this way can often be used to compare and contrast with one already undertaken.

INDOOR
The overarching point of designing your own Trail and the Trails projects in general is to get children outside and engaging with a range of outdoor environments. Occasionally there is value in carrying out an indoor Trail, e.g. to compare the results with those gathered on the same Trail in an outdoor location, or where they are exploring particular concepts, e.g. electricity, materials, etc.

COMBINED APPROACH

The design of a bespoke Trail is likely to involve a combination of these approaches. But whichever approach is taken, the result will be a unique Trail experience for the children.

FURTHER SUPPORTING RESOURCES

Additional resources for many Trails can be found on the PSTT website.

CONCLUSION

These w are just the start — what's in the outdoors where you are? How can you make the most of the school' grounds, urban spaces, rural spaces, city farms, churchyards, parks, gardens, woodlands, coasts, outdoor centres, wilderness areas, supermarkets or leisure centres close to you? Can you develop and customise these Trails to include new locations of your own choice?

The Trails projects have had significant impact in many schools and on many levels. Children were enthused and learned so much more than they expected from going outdoors; teachers were inspired to find new locations and themes to make their lessons and topics more interesting and school leaders were genuinely surprised at the change in culture that these projects brought to their settings.

Here are some quotes from teachers in the STEM Trails project:

"Children's enthusiasm is overwhelming. Children are keen to be out on a Trail again - they are driving the project!"

"Planning a Trail has reignited enthusiasm for teachers in particular topics."

"Pupils' concept of learning beyond the classroom has been greatly enhanced."

"One teacher's realisation that STEM Trails can be carried out in the immediate environment as opposed to 'paid' trips to local establishments was transformative."

"Over the year, the confidence in teaching staff to go outside and try different Trails has increased."

SO WHAT ARE YOU WAITING FOR? 'LET'S GO!'

REFERENCES

Cottrell, S., Radik-Cottrell, J. (2010) *Benefits of outdoor skills to health, learning and lifestyle: A literature review: Association of Fish & Wildlife Agencies' North America Conservation Education Strategy*

Dillion, J. *et al* (2010) *Education outside the classroom. Research report RR802 DfES/NFER*

Grimshaw, M., Curwen, L., Morgan, J., Shallcross, K.R., Franklin, S.D. & Shallcross, D.E (2019) 'The benefits of outdoor learning on science teaching', *J. Emergent Science*, **16**, **40-45** (2019)

Morgan, J., Franklin, S.D. & Shallcross, D.E. (2017) 'Science Trails', *J. Emergent Science*, **13**, **31-35** (2017)

OFSTED (2008) *Learning outside the classroom: How far should you go?* HMSO: London

HEALTH & SAFETY CHECKLIST

Trails

LOCATION:

DATE:

BEFORE TRAIL
Preventative

Appropriate clothing and footwear	☐
Check for stab hazards	☐
Appropriate adult to child ratio	☐
Check for allergies	☐
Check medical needs of class	☐
Have appropriate medication	☐
Ensure that children stay hydrated	☐
Ensure that children are aware of water hazards e.g. lakes and rivers	☐
Ensure that children are aware of electrical hazards	☐
General medical kit	☐
Ensure that children know how to use equipment safely	☐

DURING TRAIL
Awareness

Be aware of traffic and busy roads	☐
Be sure to point out potential stab hazards to children	☐
Warn children to be careful around sound and light extremes	☐
Care when walking, e.g. dog mess and litter	☐
Animal welfare – ensure that children do not disturb local wildlife	☐
Wash hands upon returning to school	☐
Ensure that adult helpers/children are aware of triggers of allergies	☐
Point out potential water hazards	☐
Point out potential electrical hazards	☐
Ensure that children stay hydrated	☐
Accessible medical kit	☐
Ensure that children are using equipment safely	☐

SPECIFIC CHILDREN IDENTIFIED:

Name	Need	Action required

Let's Go! 2D AND 3D SHAPES – KS1

WHAT SHAPES CAN WE FIND IN OUR SCHOOL AND BEYOND?

INTRODUCTION

This Trail aims for children to identify common 2D and 3D shapes in the environment. The children will investigate a number of key concepts associated with shapes, including their names and properties and whether they are regular or irregular. They will observe how they are used and where they are found. This Trail may be completed in your school and playground, or you could compare and contrast your school and its grounds with locations beyond the school to give children a wider experience. This is also an opportunity to assess what children already know and identify their next steps. This Trail links with a variety of topics, such as 'Homes' or 'Buildings', or may be used to make a maths lesson on shape more relevant or interesting.

CONCEPTS/OBJECTIVES EXPLORED

- Identify and name common 2D and 3D shapes.
- Use mathematical vocabulary linked to 2D and 3D shapes.
- Describe their properties, including number of sides, faces, corners, edges, etc.
- Understand the terms regular and irregular.

KEY VOCABULARY

Shape
Square
Cube
Rectangle/Oblong
Cuboid
Triangle
Pyramid
Triangular prism
Circle
Sphere
Cone
Cylinder
Pentagon
Hexagon
Straight
Curve
Corner/Right angle
Edge
Side
Face

LOCATION

- 2 locations in the school building
- 2 locations in the playground
- 2 locations beyond the school grounds

SCIENTIFIC SKILLS

- Observing
- Recording
- Collecting data
- Presenting results
- Drawing conclusions based on evidence

INVESTIGATION TYPE

- Exploration
- Survey
- Classification

RESOURCES AND PREPARATION

- Ask the children to identify suitable locations in and around the school, e.g. playground, where they are likely to find examples of a variety of shapes. Ask them to justify their reasons.
- Ask the children to predict what shapes they think they might see and why?
- If the intention is to use the Trail to assess the children's current understanding of shape (e.g. the names and properties that are known), this may be done on the Trail.
- If the Trail is to be used to determine how the children can apply their knowledge of shape, ensure that any key vocabulary or concepts are taught in advance.
- Some children will need support, such as examples of common shapes or a shape identification sheet.

Each group needs:

Digital cameras
Clipboards
Pencils/pens
Paper or tally chart proforma
Flat shapes
3D shapes
Sound buttons or tablet computer for recording responses

ON THE TRAIL

WHAT TO DO

- **Activity 1**: Walk around as a class, looking for shapes within the environment. Some shapes may be found in isolation, whereas others may be within or part of a structure. Ask key questions 1 – 3.
- **Activity 2**: Ask the children to choose a shape and find 3 examples in the environment. They should either record or photograph these (ensuring the flat shape/vocabulary card is in the photograph). Ask them to look for examples that are different sizes and made of different materials.
- **Activity 3**: Ask the children to look for shapes that have the following properties and record or photograph them (you can add to this list or modify it depending on the age of the children):

  A straight line (or edge)

  A corner (or right angle)

  A circular edge

  A shape with 3 sides and/or a 3D shape with a triangular face

  A shape with 4 sides and/or a 3D shape with a square/rectangular face

  A shape with 5 sides and/or a 3D shape with a pentagonal face

  A regular shape

  An irregular shape

  A shape with an acute angle

  A shape with an obtuse angle

  A shape with the greatest number of vertices.

- **Activity 4**: Ask key question 4. Children could complete a tally chart of common 2D and 3D shapes.
- **Activity 5**: Ask key questions 5 and 6. Ask the children to photograph or record the most unusual shape they can see.
- Ask key question 7.
- Go to a new location and repeat, or finish the Trail in school.

KEY QUESTIONS

- 1 Can you name each of the shapes we can see?
- 2 Can you tell me something about the shape you can see?
- 3 What are the properties of this shape?
- 4 What is the most common shape we can see?
- 5 What is the most unusual (irregular) shape you can find?
- 6 Why is it unusual – what are its properties?
- 7 What shapes didn't we see?

BACK IN THE CLASSROOM

- Discuss what shapes were seen and why some shapes were regularly found and others were not.
- Ask the children to record the properties of their shapes on post-it notes, attaching these to their photographs or drawings.
- Ask the children to create graphs or pictograms using data collected, answering the questions: Which were the most common/least common shapes? How do you know that?
- Children could use their knowledge of the shapes seen in the environment to design a structure related to their topic.

Let's Go! 2D AND 3D SHAPES – KS2

WHAT SHAPES CAN WE FIND IN OUR SCHOOL AND BEYOND?

ages 7-11

INTRODUCTION

This Trail aims to expand on the ideas and activities used in the KS1 Shape Trail, extending the vocabulary the children use to describe 2D and 3D shapes in the environment. The children will continue to investigate a number of key concepts associated with shapes and observe how they are used and where they are found. The children will be encouraged to name more complex shapes or use more technical vocabulary. You could complete this Trail in your school and playground, or you could compare and contrast your school and its grounds with locations beyond the school to give children a wider experience. It is also an opportunity to assess what is already known and to consider next steps. This Trail can link with a variety of topics, be part of a maths week or be used to make a maths lesson on shape more relevant or interesting.

KEY VOCABULARY

Horizontal

Vertical

Perpendicular

Parallel

Quadrilateral

Triangle – equilateral, isosceles, scalene right angle

Reflex angle

Dimensions

Vertically opposite

Circumference

Radius

Diameter

Polygon

Vertices

Acute

Obtuse

Regular

Irregular

CONCEPTS/OBJECTIVES EXPLORED

- Identify and name common and less common 2D and 3D shapes.
- Use mathematical vocabulary for 2D and 3D shapes, including different quadrilaterals and triangles.
- Use appropriate vocabulary, including horizontal, vertical, perpendicular, parallel, various angles, etc., to describe shapes.
- Describe the features of circular shapes including circumference, radius and diameter.

LOCATION

- 2 locations in the school building
- 2 locations in the playground
- 2 locations beyond the school grounds

SCIENTIFIC SKILLS

- Observing
- Recording
- Collecting data
- Presenting results
- Drawing conclusions based on evidence

INVESTIGATION TYPE

- Exploration
- Survey
- Classification

RESOURCES AND PREPARATION

- Ask the children what shapes they would expect to find outdoors; where these might be and their purpose; and where they would expect to see the greatest range of shapes. Debate whether the children should go to one location, or compare and contrast locations to see which one has more shapes. Consider a vote on which approach they would prefer.
- If the intention is to use the Trail to assess the children's current understanding of shape (e.g. the names and properties that are known), this may be done on the Trail.
- If the Trail is to be used to determine how the children can apply their knowledge of shape, ensure that any key vocabulary or concepts are taught in advance.

Each group needs:

Digital cameras

Clipboards

Pencils/pens

Paper or tally chart proforma

Vocabulary cards with key properties of shapes on them as well as names of shapes

Sound buttons or tablet computer for recording responses

 ON THE TRAIL

WHAT TO DO

- **Activity 1**: Walk around as a class, looking for shapes within the environment. Some shapes may be found in isolation, whereas others may be within or part of a structure. Ask key questions 1 – 3.
- **Activity 2**: Using vocabulary strips or cards, ask the children to find an example of some of these quadrilaterals: square, rectangle, parallelogram, rhombus, irregular quadrilateral, trapezium, isosceles trapezium, kite, and name those they have located . Ask them to find examples of 3 different triangles (for example: equilateral, isosceles, scalene, or right angle) and name these. Ask the children to record or photograph each example (making sure that the vocabulary card is in the photograph), looking for examples that are different sizes and made of different materials.
- **Activity 3**: Ask the children to look for shapes or lines that include one or more of the following properties and record or photograph these (you can add to this list or modify it depending on the age of the children). They should state whether each is a 2D or 3D shape. If it is helpful, the children could use chalk to mark angles, or use a protractor to measure these.
- **Activity 4**: Ask key question 4. Complete a tally chart of some of the properties found above, depending on what you want the children to focus on.
- **Activity 5**: Ask key questions 5 and 6. Ask the children to photograph or record the most unusual shape they can see. Examples are:

A horizontal line	Vertically opposite angles (look at examples of lines crossing each other)
A vertical line	
A perpendicular line	2 circles with different sizes of circumference
Parallel lines	
An acute angle	2 different lengths of radius (if possible measure them so that the circumference can be calculated back in class)
A right angle	
A reflex angle	2 different lengths of diameter (as above)

- Ask key question 7.
- Go to a new location and repeat, or finish the Trail in school.

?

KEY QUESTIONS

- 1 Can you name each of the shapes we can see?
- 2 Can you tell me something about the shape you can see?
- 3 What are the properties of this shape?
- 4 What is the most common shape property you can see?
- 5 What is the most unusual (irregular) shape you can find?
- 6 Why is it unusual – what are its properties?
- 7 What shapes didn't we see?

 ## BACK IN THE CLASSROOM

- Research the names of 2D and 3D shapes that were unknown to the children, e.g. ellipsoid – balloon.
- Discuss why certain shapes are used for specific purposes (e.g. Why are tables rectangular/circular in classrooms? Why might other shapes not be used?). Look at paving stones. How does their shape affect the way they fit together? Consider investigating various shapes for tables/paving stones, etc.
- If children have visited a playpark or have play equipment in their playground, they could use their knowledge of shapes to design their own piece of equipment, as a model or drawing.

Let's Go! ALGORITHMS

WHAT INSTRUCTIONS ARE FOLLOWED IN THE WORLD AROUND US?

INTRODUCTION

This Trail aims to introduce children to the concept of algorithms and how these are used in everyday life. It was inspired by the work of June Isik and a group of Reception children in her local area. Algorithms are simply a set of instructions that need to be followed in order to solve a problem or complete an activity. These instructions are often unseen. The Trail encourages children to observe an outcome and articulate instructions needed to achieve this. It encourages children to appreciate that technology works because it is programmed to follow instructions. It is also important that children recognise that there are numerous sets of instructions that could have the same outcome and they often need to choose the most efficient algorithm. They will be encouraged to identify non-verbal instructions and observe the cause and effect of programmes (such as responses to traffic lights by drivers).

CONCEPTS/OBJECTIVES EXPLORED

- That algorithms are a set of instructions given to complete a task.
- That different sets of instructions can produce the same outcome.
- That people and technology follow algorithms.
- That algorithms are the basis for computer programming.

KEY VOCABULARY

Algorithm
Instruction
Problem-solving
Task
Outcome
Computer programme
Human
Machine

LOCATION

- Town or village centre with traffic lights and people using technology

SCIENTIFIC SKILLS

- Observing
- Measuring
- Recording
- Collecting data
- Presenting results
- Drawing conclusions based on evidence

INVESTIGATION TYPE

- Exploration
- Survey
- Classification
- Pattern seeking

RESOURCES AND PREPARATION

- Discuss the meaning of 'algorithm' and give the children sets of instructions to follow (with increasing complexity) depending on their age.
- Ask the children to write or talk about their own algorithms for getting ready for school or bed.
- Ask the children to identify examples where algorithms (specific instructions) are necessary in real life (for example, to extract money from a cash machine or stop the traffic).
- Check out your chosen route, so you can see what the children will be observing – ensure that traffic lights are included at some point.
- Plan one route to get to your chosen destination, and a different one for your return. One should be the shortest way. Follow these routes on the Trail.

Each group needs:

Digital cameras

Tablet computers – for recording instructions and filming

Sound buttons or other audio-recording device if needed

Clipboards

Pens/pencils

Paper or prepared crib sheet

Stopwatch

ON THE TRAIL

WHAT TO DO

- Explain to the children that they will be following two different routes to get to and from the destination of the Trail. Ask them to think about the instructions they are following to get to their destination.
- Once at the destination, split the class into 3 groups, each supported by one or more adult helper. Each group will complete 3 activities, but at different times.

Group 1/Activity 1: Human algorithms
- Ask this group to observe people interacting with their environment. Ask the children to create a set of instructions that these people might be following to complete their activities. Children can either write them down or record their findings using a device such as a sound button or tablet computer. Take photographs if possible and appropriate. Ask key question 1. Ask whether the children can see non-verbal clues that instruct people to stop or go? Ask key questions 2 and 3. Move onto Activity 2.

Group 2/Activity 2: Technological algorithms
- Ask this group to observe machines working around them. Ask the children to verbalise the instructions being followed by machines or other man-made devices. You may need to look through a shop window, or visit a shop to do this. Ask key questions 4 – 6 (you may need to substitute the questions). Ask them to observe any other technology that is following a programme or set of instructions. Children record their findings as above. Move onto Activity 3.

Group 3/Activity 3: Traffic lights
- Ask this group to focus on a set of traffic lights and verbalise the instructions these are giving to drivers. Record the sequence by filming it or writing it down. Depending on the age of the children, use a stopwatch to time the length of each sequence. Ask why the sequence lasts for this long on each colour? What if it were longer or shorter? Move onto Activity 1.
- When the Trail is complete, take a different route back to school, asking the children to think about the change to the route.

KEY QUESTIONS

- 1 Could the people achieve their task given a different set of instructions?
- 2 Can you see a colour that is used to give the instructions 'stop', 'no' or 'cancel'?
- 3 Can you see a colour that is used to give the instructions 'yes' or 'go'?
- 4 What instructions are automatic doors following?
- 5 What instructions are bar code readers following?
- 6 What instructions are cashpoint machines or chip and pin machines following?

BACK IN THE CLASSROOM

Discuss with the children why they took different routes to and from the Trail destination. Draw out the concept that there can be more than one set of instructions for the same outcome. Ask the children which was the best route and why? Relate this to how a computer can achieve the same tasks given different algorithms. Play a game of 'Find the Number' using different operations. Which calculation requires the greatest number of operations? Which requires the fewest? Relate this to achieving the same outcome from different algorithms.

Let's Go! AQUARIUM

INTRODUCTION

This Trail aims to encourage children to consider animals that live in aquatic habitats. They will observe which of the animals' features help them to live in these environments, as well as considering the wide variety of animals that aquatic habitats support. This Trail will support teachers and children to make the most of their experience at an aquarium. This is a good opportunity to look at animal adaptations in detail and compare and contrast aquatic animals observed on the visit with ones the children have seen or know about that live in waters in this country. It could also provide opportunities for children to find out more about animals that populate rivers or the sea here, such as seals or dolphins.

KEY VOCABULARY

Aquarium
Aquatic
Fish – tail, fin, scales, gills
Crab – crustacean
Jellyfish
Seahorse
Seal
Vertebrate/Invertebrate
Fish/Mammal/
Amphibian/Reptile/Bird
Turtle
Eel
Stingray
Starfish
Salt water
Fresh water
Mangrove
Carnivore
Herbivore
Omnivore
Tentacle
Sting
Electric shock

CONCEPTS/OBJECTIVES EXPLORED

- Animals live around the world in a variety of habitats.
- Animals are adapted to their habitats.
- Animals can be herbivores, omnivores or carnivores.
- Animals have features that can identify them as herbivores, omnivores or carnivores.

LOCATION

- An aquarium

SCIENTIFIC SKILLS

- Observing
- Measuring
- Recording
- Collecting data

INVESTIGATION TYPE

- Exploration
- Survey
- Classification
- Pattern seeking

RESOURCES AND PREPARATION

Each group needs:

Digital camera

Tablet computers

Laminated cards with animal names on

Pedometers

When recording, use age appropriate methods – photographs and sound buttons/verbal recording devices/filming for younger/less confident children. The same and written recording for older/more confident children

Before the visit, children (in groups) could choose between 3 and 6 contrasting animals to observe at the aquarium. The teacher could direct choices to ensure that they are diverse – choose an animal that lives in salt water, fresh water, tropical water or cold water, etc., and children could look at the aquarium's webpage to make their choices of animal in advance. They could plan the route that they intend to take, marking on the map where they are likely to see their animals. Other themes could also be selected around specific adaptations, such as looking for herbivores, carnivores or omnivores; vertebrates or invertebrates; how animals use camouflage; or, if looking at a particular place, e.g. Africa, animals that are indigenous to the waters of this continent.

ON THE TRAIL

WHAT TO DO

To provide an opportunity for maths/data collection, the children could all wear pedometers to measure how far they walk on their visit.

Once the children are in their groups, refer to the route they have planned on their maps and walk to the first tank. For each of the key questions below and for those included in this section, always follow up with, 'Why do you think this?'/ 'How do you know?' to ensure that children can give evidence for their thoughts or ideas. Repeat activities for all the enclosures/animals visited.

- As the children are likely to be very excited on approaching a tank, look at the fish/creature first. Spend some time just observing it: how it moves, behaves, eats, etc. What are the features of the fish/aquatic animal? What colour is it? Are there any patterns on it? Was it easy to spot in the tank? Is it large or small? Is it with similar fish of the same species, or is it sharing the space with other water creatures? Do you think it is a vertebrate or invertebrate? What evidence do you have for this? Ask key questions 1 and 2. Can the animal be touched (ensure that this is supervised if allowed)? If it can, why is this permitted? If not, why not?

- Look for evidence about what the animal eats. Ask key questions 3 and 4.

- Describe the habitat. What plants, rocks or other natural things can be seen in the habitat (for hiding, camouflage, to eat, etc)?. Ask key questions 5 and 6. Ask the children to record this.

- Describe the tank itself. How does it keep the animals in and humans out? What materials have been used to make these strong and safe but to ensure that the animals can still be seen? Ask key questions 7 and 8. Take photographs of the tank.

- Record or photograph any additional information about the animal, e.g. in which country/waters is the animal indigenous and any other information that the children find interesting.

?

KEY QUESTIONS

- 1 Is the tank or enclosure large or small?
- 2 Is the size of the aquatic animal related to the size of its tank?
- 3 Is the animal a carnivore, herbivore or omnivore?
- 4 What features of the animal give you clues about what it eats? (Teeth, tentacles, etc.)
- 5 Have many things been added to the tank, or is it almost bare?
- 6 Is the tank heated in some way?
- 7 How does the tank safeguard both the animal and the public?
- 8 What shapes have been used to construct the tank/enclosure, etc.?

 BACK IN THE CLASSROOM

- Use evidence that children have recorded about different animals, their habitats and adaptations to compare non-indigenous animals to those found in this country and its waters. What water animals do the children have living near them? What are the similarities and differences?
- Discuss how the enclosures or tanks were constructed. Could the children construct a tank or water enclosure of their own back at school?
- For older children, look into ethical debates about aquariums and their purpose. How do they help with conservation? How is the welfare of the animals ensured?

 **BOATS**

WHAT FORCES ARE IN ACTION IN A WATER ENVIRONMENT?

INTRODUCTION

This Trail aims to explore the science themes of forces: pushes/pulls, water resistance, upthrust, floating and sinking and also materials in context, by taking a closer look at boats and their uses. The children could think about engineering and technology through observing and discussing obstacles presented by water environments and how these have been overcome. They will look at how boats are built, stored and moored, as well as their different purposes, sizes and shapes. They could investigate additional forces such as those in levers and pulleys by observing their uses on the boats, in locks working at a canal or marina, or when boats are raised from/lowered into the water. They could consider the choices of materials used to support boats being built or stored. The children could also observe how water levels can vary and what is done to overcome this where necessary.

CONCEPTS/OBJECTIVES EXPLORED

- Identify and name a number of forces in context.
- Identify the effects of water resistance and friction that act between moving surfaces.
- Identify the effects of air/wind resistance.
- Recognise that some mechanisms, including levers, pulleys and gears, allow a smaller force to have a greater effect.
- Identify and compare the suitability of a variety of everyday materials for particular uses.

KEY VOCABULARY

Boats
Floating
Sinking
Water resistance
Upthrust/Buoyancy
Friction
Pulley
Lever
Gear/Cog
Lock
Marina
Canal
Balanced forces
Unbalanced forces
Sails
Air/wind resistance

LOCATION

Anywhere children can see boats both in and out of water:
- Marina
- Canal
- Dockyard
- Sailing club

SCIENTIFIC SKILLS

- Observing
- Measuring
- Recording
- Collecting data

INVESTIGATION TYPE

- Exploration
- Survey
- Classification
- Pattern seeking

RESOURCES AND PREPARATION

- Make contact with the relevant people at the location you intend to visit, especially if it is a large dockyard or marina. This is to ensure that they can cater for a class of children safely and possibly guide you to the best things to see whilst out on the Trail.
- Discuss with the children the basic structure of a boat, as well as why it is made like this, prior to the trip. This ensures the children have a working vocabulary to draw on when on the Trail.
- Look at different types of boats and their uses. How are boats used today compared with how they were used in the past? How are/were boats used for leisure or industry? How do they differ in shape and size?

Each group needs:

Digital camera
Tablet computer
Clipboards
Prepared tables
Paper
Pens/pencils
Time lapse photography would be an excellent tool to use here

ON THE TRAIL

WHAT TO DO

- On arrival, ask the children about the kinds of boat there are, whether they are big or small and if they can identify their uses? From what materials have the boats been constructed? Record their findings.
- Examine a boat that is out of the water. Look at the structure of the boat and its shape. Can the children name any of the parts of the boat, e.g. keel.
- Once different parts of the boat's structure have been identified, ask the children about the functional purpose of each of the parts. Why does it have a keel? Ask key questions 1, 2 & 3.
- If possible, find a boat being built or repaired. How is the boat being constructed or repaired? What problems are being overcome?
- Now look at boats in water.
- Ask the children to annotate a diagram of a boat they can see with forces from the list below (choose the vocabulary most appropriate for your group of children):
    Push
    Pull
    Upthrust/buoyancy
    Friction
    Water resistance
    Air/Wind resistance
    Thrust/propulsion
    Balanced or unbalanced forces
- Ask key question 4.
- Ask the children how the boats are moored and how people access the boats? How have these structures been engineered and from what materials have they been constructed?
- If possible, observe a boat going into or coming out of the water. What equipment or machinery is being used and how does it work (e.g. a trailer with wheels for smaller boats, cranes for larger boats)? Ask key question 5.
- Ask the children to observe and record features of the wider environment; include natural features, buildings, other structures (e.g. cranes) and any wildlife.
- Ask key questions 5 – 8.

?

KEY QUESTIONS

- 1 Can the children see what would propel it? (Sails/wind, a propeller/engine, etc.)
- 2 Can they find examples of these mechanisms, such as pulleys, levers and gears?
- 3 Discuss the purpose of these mechanisms.
- 4 What are the forces involved and how do they affect the boat's movement?
- 5 What forces are in action?
- 6 Is the waterway tidal and how do the children know this? Are there waves? Is it moving?
- 7 Is the water level in your location always the same? What clues are there that it is or is not?
- 8 How have engineers overcome issues around boats encountering different depths of water? E.g. a lock in a canal, launching a boat from a beach.

BACK IN THE CLASSROOM

- Children could compare and contrast waterway use now and in the past.
- They could look at a map of the waterways in this country, how they are linked and plan a journey from one place to another.
- Children could design and make their own boats to solve a problem: e.g. make the fastest boat; or make a boat that can hold the biggest mass. What materials will they use? What materials would be good for buoyancy or waterproofing? What shape or size should the boat be? Will their boats need a keel? How will they be powered?

Let's Go! ELECTRICITY IN ACTION 2

INTRODUCTION

This Trail aims for children to consider the importance of electricity for businesses and then test their theories about which businesses use the most appliances. Their focus is to predict the appliances/uses they will find and to decide on the best location to visit. This Trail is completely child-led; each group should vote on where they want to visit from the range of shops available to them locally. The children will be encouraged to consider the variety of local shops and what would happen in different locations if the electricity failed. They will also look at how electricity is used on the streets, such as for street lighting or traffic lights and by observing people walking by (using personal devices) and will complete a survey to record their results.

KEY VOCABULARY

Electricity
Appliance
Portable
Battery
Mains powered
Electricity meter

CONCEPTS/OBJECTIVES EXPLORED

- Electricity is a form of energy.
- Electricity is used to power a range of appliances.
- Electricity is important to our everyday lives.
- Electricity is bought and an electricity meter shows how much has been used.

LOCATION

- Shops close to your school that use or have a number of electrical appliances

SCIENTIFIC SKILLS

- Observing
- Recording
- Collecting data
- Presenting results
- Drawing conclusions based on evidence
- Choosing a scientific approach to use

INVESTIGATION TYPE

- Exploration
- Survey
- Classification

RESOURCES AND PREPARATION

Each group needs:

Digital camera
Clipboards
Survey proforma/crib sheet
Pens/pencils
Tablet computer

- Ask the children to list all the local shops or businesses that they think use electrical appliances. What types of appliances are used and why? If they need some direction, give them a list of local businesses near to your school, such as hairdressers, coffee shops/cafés, launderettes/dry cleaners, etc. Focus on shops that use appliances, rather than just electricity in general.

- Ask the children to predict which shop or business is likely to have or use the most electrical appliances and decide as a group where they most want to visit to test their theory.

- Devise a class list of all the shops the children want to visit and contact them in advance of the Trail to ensure that it is appropriate for groups of children to visit.

ON THE TRAIL

WHAT TO DO

- Split the class into two groups. One group will conduct the survey of how electricity is used on the streets. The other half will further split into smaller groups to visit the shop/business of their choice, each with an adult helper. At a pre-arranged time, the groups will meet up and change activity.

- **Activity 1:** Find a place to stand where the children can observe and tally/ list all the fixed things that use electricity in the street. Ask them to look around and identify examples of electricity in use, e.g.

Traffic lights	Entry systems – phone/buzzer/touch code
Street lights	Automatic doors
Car park barriers	CCTV
Cashpoint machines	Ticket machines

- Next, ask the children to list/tally all the examples of portable/moving devices using electricity that they observe. e.g.

 Mobile phones
 Mp3 players/musical devices
 Cars/lorries/other vehicles
 Mobility scooters

- Make observations in this location for 5 – 10 minutes and then move to a different location for more examples.

- **Activity 2:** On arrival at the shop/business that your group has chosen, ask the children to record (quietly), creating a list and photographing all the appliances they can see being used or displayed.

- Once they have exhausted all possibilities, see if the manager of the shop or a member of staff can show them, or describe to them, any appliances that cannot be seen from the shop floor, e.g. washing machines, tumble dryers, kettles, etc.

- Ask the shop manager or member of staff if they have ever had a power cut? What happened? Was the business still able to operate?

- Ask about their annual electricity bill and whether this is one of the most expensive outgoings of the business. How do they try to reduce their energy bill?

KEY QUESTIONS

- 1 How many 'fixed' things did you see in the streets that use electricity?
- 2 How many 'portable' things did you see in the streets that use electricity?
- 3 Which shop had the greatest number of appliances? Why?
- 4 Which shop had the smallest number of appliances? Why?
- 5 Which shop had the most expensive electricity bill? Why?
- 6 Which shop did the most to reduce their electricity bill? How did they do this?
- 7 Was your prediction correct? Did your group go to the shop with the greatest number of electrical appliances?

BACK IN THE CLASSROOM

- Present the information from Activities 1 and 2 using their own choice of computer package. What did their results tell them? What conclusions have they reached?
- Create a mini traffic light control circuit.
- Look at how electricity is generated — carbon-based, nuclear and renewable methods. What are the advantages and disadvantages to these? Write or have a debate.
- Look at the wider issues of electrical consumption. What happens if we continue to use as much as we are using now? Can the children find ways of lowering the amount of electricity they use at school or at home?

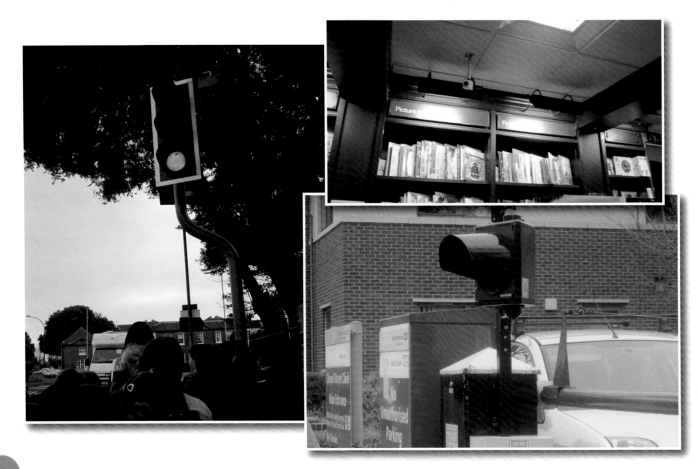

 **ELECTRICITY IN SCHOOL**

WHICH SCHOOL APPLIANCES USE MAINS ELECTRICITY, BATTERIES OR BOTH TO POWER THEM?

INTRODUCTION

This Trail aims to help children understand that electricity can come from mains power and/or batteries. It will help the children to identify that different appliances or devices need different amounts of power. The children will look at: the power sources that are used inside the school and in the school grounds; how many examples of devices powered by electricity they can find; whether there is a correlation between the size of the device or appliance and its power source. This Trail provides a good opportunity to draw the children's attention to electrical safety – the warnings children can see on electrical devices and what precautions need to be taken. They will collect ideas and examples, and then categorise them by use, function and risk, whilst considering the amount of power needed to make them work.

CONCEPTS/OBJECTIVES EXPLORED

- Electricity is a form of energy.
- Electricity can come from mains power or from batteries.
- Different amounts of electrical power are needed for different devices.
- Electricity can be dangerous and precautions should be taken.

KEY VOCABULARY

Sources of electricity
Power
Energy
Mains
Batteries
Appliance/device

LOCATION

- Inside the school
- In the school grounds

SCIENTIFIC SKILLS

- Observing
- Measuring
- Recording
- Collecting data
- Presenting results

INVESTIGATION TYPE

- Exploration
- Survey
- Classification

 ### RESOURCES AND PREPARATION

Each group needs:

Clipboard
Pencils/pens
Digital Camera

- Before you begin the Trail, ask the children to create a list of devices that they know use mains or battery power. Alternatively, provide images and ask the children to sort these. How do they know whether they are mains or battery powered? What are the differences? Are there devices that are both battery and mains powered? The children could use a Venn diagram to re-sort their list/photographs.
- The Trail may be child-led, where groups of children choose 4 locations (2 inside, 2 in the school grounds), or teacher-led. Ask the children where they think they will see the most devices or appliances that use electricity.
- Show the children how electricity is made (mains and battery power) using a short video clip.

ON THE TRAIL

WHAT TO DO

- Depending on whether you have additional adult support, group the children and ask them to go to the locations that have been decided. If not, walk to the locations as a class.
- At each location, ask the children to identify which devices are mains-powered or battery-powered. Ask key questions 1 – 3.
- Ask the children to collect photographic evidence, record lists, sketches or diagrams of what they have found.
- Look at the mains powered devices/appliances. Ask the children to explain how the electricity reaches them. Can the children see how electricity reaches the building?
- Ask the children to record the most interesting device they have found, either by sketching it or photographing it and explain why they think this. What does it do? How would life be different without it?
- Ask the children to think about electrical safety. Ask key question 4. Are there any obvious warnings on the device or appliance? Are there any indications that the device or appliance has been checked to see if it is safe? What could the dangers be with the particular devices/appliances they are looking at? Ask key question 5.
- Ask the children to list the function of each appliance. What is its job? Why was it invented?
- Ask the children to look at different types of switch. Do they work differently (e.g. light sensors in classrooms or traditional switches)?. Why are pull cords used in bathrooms instead of push switches?
- If it is possible, ask the site-manager/caretaker if the children can view the electricity meter in school. They could also look at the school's energy efficiency certificate.

KEY QUESTIONS

- 1 How many examples can you find of electrical devices powered by batteries?
- 2 How many examples can you find of electrical devices powered by the mains?
- 3 How many examples can you find of electrical devices powered by either mains or batteries or both?
- 4 Where in the school can you find signs to do with electrical safety/dangers?
- 5 Why do some electrical devices need safety signs whilst others do not?

BACK IN THE CLASSROOM

- Ask the children to create bar graphs of their findings: mains/battery/both, by location, or their function.
- Find out the difference between amps and volts and ask the children to present this to the class.
- Explore 'what if' scenarios about having no electricity – this could lead to 'switch off' day in class.
- Create simple electrical circuits (e.g. for a torch or a fan). Build their own switches from common materials.
- Ask the children to look at energy efficiency. Make a poster.

Let's Go! EXPLORING THE WORLD

WHAT ARE THE SIMILARITIES AND DIFFERENCES BETWEEN MY PLAYGROUND AND MY LOCAL PARK?

INTRODUCTION

This Trail aims to allow children to explore the similarities and differences between their school playground and a local park. They will focus on the different materials used to make the equipment, the size of the park, shapes, colours, types of activity and environmental differences, e.g. are there more trees in our playground or the park and why? They will also observe the use of signs in both locations and their purposes. This Trail has been used to run alongside topics such as 'I'm Special' or 'All About Me', which focus on what makes a child unique and how they might be different from/similar to their friends.

CONCEPTS/OBJECTIVES EXPLORED

- To know about similarities and differences in relation to places, objects, materials and living things.
- To talk about the features of their own immediate environment and how environments might vary from one another.

KEY VOCABULARY

Materials
Shape
Plastic
Wood
Metal
Rubber
Sign

LOCATION

- Playground
- A local play park

SCIENTIFIC SKILLS

- Observing
- Recording
- Collecting data
- Drawing conclusions based on evidence

INVESTIGATION TYPE

- Exploration
- Survey
- Classification

RESOURCES AND PREPARATION

- During the children's play sessions outside at school, they should be questioned about the general appearance/layout of the playground and what equipment it has in it. They should also use these sessions to identify and label different materials and what they are used for.
- It would also be helpful if children had some experience of handling different materials such as wood, plastic, metal and rubber, so that they are able to identify these materials accurately in their playgrounds and whilst on the Trail.
- Children should also look at the signs in the playground, discover what they say and their purpose. Are they to warn or inform the children? What words are used? Children could take photographs of the signs they see in the school grounds.

Each group needs:

Digital camera
Clipboards, pencils and paper
Risk assessment
Sound buttons
Stop watches
Speech bubbles

 ON THE TRAIL

WHAT TO DO

- Walk in groups of 2 or 3, to a local play park, preferably with an adult helper to support each group.
- Observe the features you see on the way to the park, such as buildings, cars, the road, the pavement, trees, plants, etc. Discuss materials observed along the route. Where have the children seen similar or different objects before?

At the park:
- Stand as a group and observe the features of the park – open spaces, trees, plants, the playground equipment, etc.
- Ask the children key questions 1 – 4.
- The children should observe how the playground equipment is made and the materials used. Children should be challenged to say why these materials are used. They should use their senses of sight and touch to help them determine the type of material. Can the children see how the play equipment has been constructed? Why are play areas important?
- The children can then play on the different pieces of equipment to understand and describe what each one does and why the material might have been chosen to build it – is the material soft or hard? Is it rough or smooth? How does it help you swing, slide, turn, spin or climb? Do the shapes of the playground equipment enhance the children's experiences (you could ask, for example, whether they would prefer a straight or curly slide)? Why do they think this? Take photographs of the children using the different pieces of equipment.
- Sound buttons or tablet computers can be used to record the different environmental sounds and children's responses.
- Draw children's attention to the use of warning or information signs in the parks and ask them to think about creating their own using text and pictures. They should make a plan of the playground showing the different equipment and label these. Photographs should be taken of these signs as well as the play park for reference in the classroom.

KEY QUESTIONS ?

- 1 Is the play park bigger or smaller than the playground at school?
- 2 Does it have similar or different play equipment to the playground?
- 3 What materials have been used to make the play equipment?
- 4 Can the children identify the material from looking at the equipment, or do they need to find this out another way?

 BACK IN THE CLASSROOM

- The main activity will be to sort photographs of both parks into groups using various questions to prompt this. The children will then be questioned as to why each picture is in that set. They will also compare and contrast pieces of equipment designed for children of different ages (e.g. a large and small slide). Finally, the children will tally the different materials that they find in the park.
- Children could create their own warning or information signs for a park or playground.
- Use the children's play experiences as a prompt for recount or descriptive writing.

Let's Go! FOOD SHOPPING

HOW IS FOOD PREPARED, MADE, AND STORED IN A SUPERMARKET?

INTRODUCTION

This Trail aims to explore a number of science themes within a supermarket setting for younger children, such as how and why food is prepared, made and stored at different temperatures. The children will initially focus on and discuss how fresh bread is made in the bakery department, from wheat in the field to flour and then to bread in the ovens. Some supermarkets, if this is pre-arranged, will allow children to make their own bread in store. This exploration will begin to develop the children's understanding of irreversible changes, through observations and discussion. The visit also provides an opportunity for children to visit different departments within a store; find out about different varieties of meat, fish and cheese; and explore the fruit and vegetable aisles.

CONCEPTS/OBJECTIVES EXPLORED

- To talk about why things happen and how things work.
- To develop an understanding of growth, decay and changes over time.
- To look closely at similarities, differences, patterns and change.

KEY VOCABULARY

Hot
Cold
Warm
Temperature
Cool
Bread
Yeast
Flour
Water
Meat
Fish
Cheese
Fruit
Vegetable
Milk

LOCATION

- A local large supermarket

SCIENTIFIC SKILLS

- Observing
- Measuring
- Recording
- Collecting data

INVESTIGATION TYPE

- Exploration
- Survey
- Classification

RESOURCES AND PREPARATION

- Contact your local supermarket to see if the children can visit the bakery and make bread there.
- Enlist the help of parents or other adult support to ensure that adult:child ratios are appropriate, especially if walking to the store.
- Discuss with the children their experiences of supermarkets. Ask them why we might shop at a supermarket instead of smaller stores?
- Set up the role play area as a supermarket to determine children's existing knowledge.
- Show the children pictures of different foods and ask them where they would find these in a supermarket – begin to explore the idea that different foods are kept at different temperatures and pose the question, 'What do you think the hottest/coldest place will be and why'?

Each group needs:

Data loggers

Rulers

Digital thermometer will be used to log temperatures as we are on the Trail

Digital cameras used by pupils to photograph different areas within supermarket and making bread sequence

 ON THE TRAIL

WHAT TO DO

- If pre-arranged with the supermarket, go to the bakery department so that the children can make their bread. Use key questions 1 and 2 to generate their thoughts and ideas. If this has not been pre-arranged, or if you have additional time before or after the visit, complete the following activities below.
- Discuss the different areas of the store. Visit each of the areas looking at the different foods on offer. Children should take photographs of different aspects of their visit to remind them of locations for evaluation back in school. Some areas could include:

  The fruit and vegetable aisle

  The meat aisle

  The fish aisle

  The dairy aisle

  The frozen aisle

  The grocery/dry food aisles

  Any other aisles of interest to the children.

- At each location, complete the following :
- **Activity 1:** Ask the children key questions 3 – 5 below, and lots of open-ended questions (starting with 'Why do you think...?').
- **Activity 2:** When thinking about the shapes and sizes of different products, encourage the children to relate the shapes to familiar 2D or 3D ones they know and name them, such as square, rectangle, circle, cuboid, cylinder, etc. The children could estimate how big or small they think the products are, using standard or non-standard units such as their hands: 'I think it will be 3 hands long', etc. They could measure the item, using standard or non-standard units such as cm or cubes. Ask key questions 6 – 7.
- **Activity 3:** The children may also explore how different food needs to be stored at different temperatures, using the store's thermometers or their own data loggers. Measure and record the different temperatures throughout the store. Ask key question 8.
- **Activity 4:** Ask the children to find and photograph the different ingredients used in making bread: flour, yeast, salt, water, etc.

KEY QUESTIONS

- 1 What do the ingredients look like, compared to the end result (bread)?
- 2 Why might we need to use different temperatures for making bread?
- 3 What colours can be seen?
- 4 What shapes can you see?
- 5 What materials can you see?
- 6 How big do you think the item is (predict)?
- 7 How big is it (measured)?
- 8 Where is the hottest/coldest temperature located in the supermarket?

BACK IN THE CLASSROOM

- Make bread at school and draw comparisons with baking in the supermarket .
- Read 'The Little Red Hen', exploring the process of bread-making from wheat to final product.
- Share the children's findings from the Trail — what colours and shapes did they find? What was the biggest/smallest item they found?
- Look at different types of farms, in this country and around the world, to see how food is produced.
- Discuss what would happen to food if it were stored at the wrong temperature. Test out these ideas using frozen food like ice-cream; see what happens to food over time — mould growth/spoiling.

 **HISTORICAL BUILDINGS**

DO OLD BUILDINGS USE THE SAME MATERIALS AND SHAPES AS NEWER ONES?

INTRODUCTION

This Trail aims to encourage children to look at historical buildings, comparing and contrasting these with modern ones, so they can see how buildings have evolved over time. They will look at both the materials and shapes used to make the building and think about how technology and engineering were different in the past. How were construction problems solved without the use of cranes, other modern technology or tools? This Trail was originally completed by children doing a Tudor topic in school, studying Tudor houses at a local museum; however, the principles investigated could be applied to any historical building in other history topics. By looking at a common building, such as a house, the children were able to draw on their experiences of modern day buildings to ask their own questions about historical ones. Buildings used for other purposes could also be considered on this Trail.

KEY VOCABULARY

Materials
Property
Hard
Transparent
Flexible
Rigid
Natural
Brick
Stone
Lime
Mud
Wood
Wattle
Daub
Stone
Thatch
Shape
Rectangle
Square
Triangle
Hexagon
Angle
Right angle
Construction
Foundation
Walls
Roof

CONCEPTS/OBJECTIVES EXPLORED

- Materials can be used in a variety of ways.
- Materials are chosen for specific purposes depending on their properties.
- There are similarities and differences between common materials.
- Compare and classify geometric shapes, including quadrilaterals and triangles, based on their properties and sizes.

LOCATION

- Any historical building or location, e.g. museum, church, cathedral, Tudor house, castle, Roman villa

SCIENTIFIC SKILLS

- Observing
- Measuring
- Recording
- Collecting data
- Presenting results
- Drawing conclusions based on evidence

INVESTIGATION TYPE

- Exploration
- Survey
- Classification
- Changes over time

RESOURCES AND PREPARATION

- Science – look at modern day equivalents of the building you are visiting. Look at pictures; discuss what construction materials have been used and why these materials have been chosen.

- Technology – discuss how technology has improved building materials, and modern living. When were the materials invented? Who created them?

- Engineering – what is the purpose of the building and how do the children think it was constructed? What problems might the builders have faced?

- Maths – ensure that children have a good knowledge of 2D and 3D shapes, and can name these. What shapes can be seen/are used in modern day buildings and why? Remind them of key vocabulary and explain that shapes will be looked at inside and outside the building; could be used for patterns or tessellations and in furniture, etc.

Each group needs:

Digital camera
Clipboards
Paper or proforma to record the answers to questions
Pens/pencils

 ON THE TRAIL

WHAT TO DO

- Look at a building of interest and discuss both the construction materials and the shapes that can be seen in use. In their discussions about materials, ensure that the children look at the roof, walls, windows, window frames, doors, door handles and other small features. When looking at the shapes that have been used in constructing this building, ask the children to identify and name common 2D and 3D shapes.

- Work in small groups. Each group focuses on one common material and one shape (e.g. wood or glass, rectangle or triangle) and identifies and records information: where they have seen it; how frequently; how many different types of objects or buildings it has been used to make. Children should record using writing, drawing and photographs.

- As a class, discuss why these materials were chosen for this building and how they are different from or similar to those seen in buildings today. Ask key questions 1 – 4.

- Discuss why the shapes were chosen for this building and how the shapes chosen make the construction stable. Ask key questions 5 – 7.

- Ask the children to find out how the building was built (either using information displayed or by asking a member of staff). Can they see any evidence that would help them to answer this question? Can they find out what technology was used to make the building (e.g. the development of tools or practices like glass-making)? What engineering or problem-solving was needed at the time the building was constructed?

KEY QUESTIONS

- 1 How have building materials changed or developed through time?
- 2 What materials are available now that were not when this building was built? E.g. plastic in uPVC windows, etc.
- 3 Is there evidence that the building has been restored or mended using more modern materials?
- 4 What is this evidence?
- 5 Have the shapes used in this type of building changed over time?
- 6 Are there any unusual shapes or structures in this building that are not seen commonly today? E.g. domed roof, spire, etc.
- 7 What is the function of these shapes?

BACK IN THE CLASSROOM

- Look at how materials used for buildings and internal features have changed/developed over time. Children could make a poster of how the materials used to make buildings have been developed, when they were first used and their modern day equivalents, if any.
- Children could make a model of their historical building, thinking about materials they would use and how to construct it.
- Look at tessellations and patterns in the building and investigate this with other shapes, both regular and irregular. Children may also have their own investigation ideas.

Let's Go! INSECTS

WHERE IS THE BEST PLACE TO FIND INSECTS?

ages 5-11

INTRODUCTION

This Trail aims to help children to focus specifically on insects and so is best to do in the summer time when insectsare most abundant. Insects are a group of animals that are incredibly important to our world: as pollinators for crops, aerating soil and biological recycling; while others destroy crops and spread disease. Insects outnumber humans considerably and can be found on all continents, from the hottest to the coldest places. This Trail is child-led and seeks the best and worst places to find insects (both in the school grounds and beyond). This Trail links to maths through the collection of data and presenting the results, as well as promoting scientific skills such as making predictions, testing ideas and interpreting results.

CONCEPTS/OBJECTIVES EXPLORED

- Identify some insects living in their habitats.
- Recognise that environments can change and pose dangers to living things.
- Study and raise questions about the local environment.
- Use classification systems or keys to identify insects.

KEY VOCABULARY

Insect
Invertebrate
Habitat
Pollinator
Environment
Quadrat
Exoskeleton

LOCATION

- 2 locations in your school grounds
- 2 locations beyond your school grounds

SCIENTIFIC SKILLS

- Observing
- Measuring
- Recording
- Collecting data
- Presenting results
- Drawing conclusions based on evidence
- Choosing a scientific approach to use

INVESTIGATION TYPE

- Exploration
- Survey
- Classification
- Pattern seeking

RESOURCES AND PREPARATION

- Research what an insect is, consider familiar insects and what these need in a habitat to survive. Look at local habitats that would support them.
- Draw up a list of possible locations in and beyond your school that you could visit.
- Hold a class vote: where would you most expect to find insects? Ask the children to support their ideas. Choose two locations to visit, one within the school grounds and one beyond.
- Look at the list again and vote which locations would be the worst possible places to find insects. Again ask the children to back up their thinking. Choose two locations to visit (within the school grounds and beyond) where they would least expect to find insects.
- Research insects common to your area.

Each group needs:

30 cm rulers taped together to make a quadrat

Clipboards

Pencils/pens

Digital cameras

Tablet computers/ identification keys

Magnifiers or portable microscopes

 ON THE TRAIL

WHAT TO DO

- Either complete the Trail in one day or in two parts: both school locations one day and then the locations beyond the school another day.
- On the way to your first location, ask the children to look out for any insects they can find or see on the way. Ask them to think about what those insects are doing (walking, flying, pollinating, etc.). Look at the places they are found – gardens, on walls, on the pavement, etc. Explain that insects have an exoskeleton. Ask the children why this is a good idea. Can the children find examples, take photographs or think of anything else that uses this principle (such as cars, buildings, etc.)? How have we used this idea?
- Children will use quadrats to sample insects in their chosen location. At the first location, ask the children to look around to select the best area to place their quadrat.
- Ask the children to place the quadrat in their chosen location at the same time and begin the stopwatch. Each person in the group should count the insects they see in a given time. Alternatively, some could count whilst others identify the different insects seen. Remind the children that they are only allowed to count the insects that are in their little area. Initially, it may seem that there is nothing in the area. Remind the children that insects can walk or crawl into it!
- Use a tally chart to help them keep count. Ask key questions 1 – 7.
- Use an insect collector, such as a pooter or a paint brush, to collect samples of the insects that they find.
- Children could then sketch their specimens before returning them to their habitat. Insects need to eat and drink, stay away from predators and many like to stay in a place where their bodies don't dry out too much. The children could design investigations to test this.
- Encourage the children to take lots of photographs both of the insects they have counted and the habitats for further study back in class.
- Repeat these activities in the remaining 3 locations.

KEY QUESTIONS

- 1 Which location had the greatest number of insects living there?
- 2 Why do you think the habitat attracted so many insects?
- 3 Were the insects mainly ones that generally walk, fly or swim?
- 4 What was the most common insect found?
- 5 What was the least common insect found?
- 6 Which location had the fewest number of insects?
- 7 What was it about the habitat that meant they did not live there?

BACK IN THE CLASSROOM

- Look at animals or objects with an exoskeleton – an egg, a crab.
- Research helpful insects: pollinators, e.g. bees; producers of honey, wax, silk; insectivorous insects (e.g. ladybirds who eat aphids that destroy crops). Look at what is happening to them and what threat this poses to our planet. Write a persuasive piece of text to convince the head teacher or local council to increase bee-friendly habitats within the school or local area.
- Research insects that cause harm or spread disease. How are these insects being managed?
- What are scientists who study insects called?
- Design and make a new insect.

INTRODUCTION

This Trail aims to help children to explore the variety of food that comes from around the world. Many classes study another country or continent and this Trail is a good way to investigate the types of foods that are imported. It also leads to questions about how the food is produced, transported and stored to keep it fresh. Children could investigate how many miles the food has travelled. They will make comparisons between foods that are prepared in different ways in different countries (e.g. various types of bread, such as white bread, pitta, chapatti, ciabatta and brioche), considering similarities or differences. They might consider the various ways in which different cultures prepare meats (e.g. ham, prosciutto, pepperoni and salami). Many supermarkets will welcome classes to see how food is prepared in store, providing a unique experience to see mass production of food; there may also be tasting opportunities.

KEY VOCABULARY

Food
Nutrition
Carbohydrate
Fat
Protein
Vitamin
Mineral
Fruit
Vegetable
Fish
Shellfish
Red meat
White meat
Processed meat
Dried meat
Cheese
Bread
Milk
Yogurt

CONCEPTS/OBJECTIVES EXPLORED

- Look at other cultures' equivalents of common foods in our diets.
- Identify differences and similarities between these foods.
- Identify that animals, including humans, need the right type and amount of nutrition.
- Understand how a variety of ingredients are grown, reared, caught and processed.

LOCATION

- A supermarket or specialist food shop

SCIENTIFIC SKILLS

- Observing
- Recording
- Collecting data

INVESTIGATION TYPE

- Exploration
- Survey
- Classification

RESOURCES AND PREPARATION

- Research common foods from the country you are studying and how these foods deliver a healthy balanced diet.
- Research which crops are mass produced in the country being studied and what environmental factors contribute to their success (e.g. weather, climate).
- Discuss the animals or livestock that are common to farms in the country being studied. Does this country tend to have big or small farms, or a combination?
- Always contact the supermarket or specialist food shop that you are visiting prior to going. Some are happy to offer tours of a variety of areas, such as the bakery or transport loading areas, or support you with a member of staff. Some will also allow the children to taste different foods and see how they are made.

Each group needs:

Camera
Tablet computer
Clipboards
Pencils/pens

ON THE TRAIL

WHAT TO DO

- This Trail can be approached in various ways.
- The children could simply identify foods commonly found in the country they are studying, go and find these in the supermarket and compare and contrast with an equivalent local food. Ask key questions 1 – 8 in each aisle location.
- Groups, accompanied by an adult helper, should visit:
  - The fruit and vegetable aisle
  - The bakery
  - The fish and meat counters/aisle
  - The dairy aisle
  - The grocery/dry goods aisle
  - The basic food aisle (e.g flour, spices, herbs etc.).
- In each place, ask the children to identify and name the foods that are found in the country they are studying. Ask all key questions to get the children to think about and record their answers. Ask the children to record their findings in a variety of ways – photographs, writing them down in tables, etc.
- Alternatively, the children could look at different food groups, such as protein, carbohydrate, and classify the foods from the country they are studying.
- Visit each of the counters/aisles above but from a food group perspective and list all the foods by their food group. Are foods of the same group found together? If not, why not? Is it due to the way they are stored, packaged, etc. or another reason (e.g. ease of location)? How do people from the country being studied ensure that they get a balanced diet?
- Why do supermarkets in this country stock foods from another country or place? Is there a demand from the indigenous population for them, or is there a migrant population they are catering for? Children could ask the store manager their thoughts about this. Is there a big difference in the price of food from the country being investigated compared to similar foods made in this country?
- If pre-arranged: Watch how food is delivered to the store and see the larger storage areas, such as walk-in fridges and freezers. Find out if the children could either make their own bread, etc, or taste some of the food from the country they are looking at.

KEY QUESTIONS

- 1 What are the similarities and differences between equivalent foods from different countries?
- 2 Look at colours, shapes, sizes, etc, as well as where the food had travelled from or where it was produced.
- 3 What was the food's country of origin?
- 4 Is there an aisle that is exclusively for foods from other countries?
- 5 What is the prime nutritional content of the food?
- 6 Would you consider the food to be healthy or unhealthy and why?
- 7 Does the packaging/design reveal the country of origin?
- 8 Does the design of the packaging give more information about the country/culture/customs?

BACK IN THE CLASSROOM

- Children could write a report based on their visit, using the photographs and data they have collected.
- The children could create a table detailing types of food, how they arrive in this country and how they are kept fresh.
- Children could create packaging, using nets to make a 3D box to contain a particular food or new food from the country they are studying.
- Children could create a PowerPoint presentation using photographs to make a record of their visit.
- Children could research healthy/unhealthy food choices in foods available in this country.

 **MEASURE**

INTRODUCTION

This Trail aims to help children to apply their knowledge of measuring in a familiar context and was originally used as a way of assessing the children in this area of maths after a unit of work. The Trail will also help set the scene for a 'Back in the Classroom' activity in which the children design their own piece of playground equipment. The experience of 'real life' playground equipment brings an awareness of things they will need to consider when designing their own. This links to work on materials and engineering, as the children work out how to construct their piece of equipment and decide what materials to use.

CONCEPTS/OBJECTIVES EXPLORED

- To compare, describe and solve practical problems for lengths and heights (e.g. long/short, longer/shorter, tall, short, double, half).
- To measure and begin to record lengths and heights.
- To choose and use appropriate standard units to estimate and measure length/height in any direction, choosing an appropriate unit of meaurement.

KEY VOCABULARY

Length
Height
Long
Longer
Longest
Short
Shorter
Shortest
Tall
Taller
Tallest
Wide
Width
Data
Unit of measure
Millimetre (mm)
Centimetre (cm)
Metre (m)
Kilometre (km)
Ruler
Trundle wheel
Tape measure

LOCATION

- Play park

SCIENTIFIC SKILLS

- Observing
- Measuring
- Recording
- Collecting data

INVESTIGATION TYPE

- Exploration
- Survey

RESOURCES AND PREPARATION

Each group needs:

Digital cameras
Tablet computers
Clipboards
Pencils
Paper
Tape measures
Metre rulers
Trundle wheels
30cm rulers
String
Grids for recording evidence of understanding
Sound buttons

- The children should be familiar with estimating and measuring length, mass, time and capacity accurately, using suitable equipment and units. They should understand that they will be measuring length when out on the Trail.
- Look at pictures of the park you intend to visit and ask the children to suggest measuring activities that could be carried out there.
- Enlist the help of adult or parent helpers so that each group of 4/5 has an adult to support them.

ON THE TRAIL

WHAT TO DO

In groups:

- Discuss what playground equipment could be measured and allow the children to select a piece. Explain to the children that they will be measuring the whole piece of playground equipment, e.g. slide *and* ladder. Ask the children to draw the piece of equipment on which drawing they will later record the measurements they have taken.
- Ask key question 1.
- Once the children have decided what they will measure (length), ask them how they will measure it. Ask key questions 2 – 4. For groups using non-standard units of measure, e.g. their hands, ask whether the same children or different ones should take the measurements? Demonstrate what happens if two different people measure the equipment. The same unit, even if non-standard, should be used. If children select non-standard units of measurement, they should start measuring their piece of playground equipment and record the results. You should note any words that the children use that inform you of their thinking.
- If the children opt to use standard units of measure, ask the children what unit they will be using. Look at how big their piece of equipment is and show them their options using a metre stick and a ruler. Ask key question 5. Ensure that the children understand that. in using mm, they will get a much higher number as this is a very small unit of length; with m they will get a much lower number as this is a larger unit of length (or could they use a combination?).
- After confirming unit of length, ask key question 6. The children should select appropriate measuring equipment. If the playground equipment is an unusual shape, flexible measuring equipment (e.g. a tape measure or trundle wheel) may be more appropriate. Children may need to use more than one piece of measuring equipment.
- Ask key question 7. Measure the piece of playground equipment. Ask key question 8.
- Use digital cameras to record how problems are solved in measuring the equipment, as well as photographs of the equipment itself being measured, e.g. the piece of equipment next to a tape measure.

?

KEY QUESTIONS

- 1 Are you measuring mass, weight, length or capacity? How do you know?
- 2 How are you going to measure your piece of playground equipment?
- 3 What measuring equipment do you need?
- 4 What units will you use?
- 5 Will you be using mm, cm, m or km?
- 6 Which piece of equipment is most suitable to measure your piece of playground equipment and why?
- 7 Estimate the length of each section of equipment. Record your answer.
- 8 How close to your estimate were you? Record your answer.

BACK IN THE CLASSROOM

- Children should complete their records from the park, using or annotating any photographs taken to support this. They could use their data to produce a table, pictogram, or graph, etc.
- Each group could report their findings to the class, using key vocabulary to describe their results.
- Children could design and make a piece of real or imagined playground equipment based on findings at the park. They should decide how big it will be, what it will be made from and how it will be constructed. Create a display of finished models.

ages 3 - 6

INTRODUCTION

This Trail aims to encourage children to identify numbers used in the world around them. On the Number Trail, set out in your locality, the children will become 'number detectives'. They will search for objects labelled with numbers and count others along the Trail. The children will see how numbers are used in context and will have the opportunity to discuss where these are found and why these are used. This Trail could be used as an assessment opportunity to discover what the children already know and whether they can apply their knowledge and understanding of number. The Trail may be used to enhance a unit of work, either introducing children to numbers or increasing their experience.

KEY VOCABULARY

Numbers – concept of counting

Numerals – symbol or name that stands for a number, e.g. 3, 49, twelve

Digit – single symbols that are used to make numerals

Highest

Lowest

Quantity

Amount

Many

Few

More

Less

Odd

Even

Label

CONCEPTS/OBJECTIVES EXPLORED

- To develop an awareness of numbers – their use and purpose – in our local environment.
- To recognise numerals and digits up to 10.
- To recognise numerals beyond 10.
- To begin to develop explanations of their own, giving suggestions as to the purpose of using numbers to label.

LOCATION

- Village
- Housing estate
- Main road
- Shop

SCIENTIFIC SKILLS

- Observing
- Recording
- Collecting data
- Presenting results

INVESTIGATION TYPE

- Exploration
- Survey
- Classification
- Pattern seeking

RESOURCES AND PREPARATION

- Plan and walk your Trail in advance, ensuring that this provides plentiful opportunity for the children to find numbers as they walk along, and direct helpers accordingly.
- Discuss the concept of number with the class and what numerals and digits represent, if the children are old enough to appreciate the distinctions.
- Ask the children what they think numbers are used for and where they think they might see them. The children should recognise numerals up to 10 and beyond, if possible.
- Prepare number cards with quantities, or use classroom resources, to support children if necessary on the Trail.

Each group needs:

High-visibility vests
Digital cameras
Clipboards
Paper/recording sheet
Pencils/pens
Number cards with numerals and their corresponding quantities to support children if necessary
Lots of adult helpers

ON THE TRAIL

WHAT TO DO

- This Trail works best if you keep walking, stopping now and again to take photographs or recording information using a digital camera.
- Arrange the children into smaller groups with adult helpers and complete the following activities, in any order:
- **Activity 1:** Direct the children to list or photograph as many objects as possible that have numbers on them, e.g. front doors, car number plates, shop fronts, lamp posts, information on vans (e.g. phone numbers), on buses, postboxes, etc. Ask the children to look at people's clothing: do these have numbers on them? Ask key questions 1 and 2.
- **Activity 2:** Throughout the Trail, look for high/large and low/small numbers. Ask the children to find examples of high and low numbers as they are walking and photograph them. You could challenge the children to 'beat' their previously identified high or low number. Ask key questions 3 and 4..
- **Activity 3:** Ask the children to look for sequences of numbers, going up or down. House numbers are a good starting point and some lamp posts have numbers on them. Question the children about the sequence; older children should discuss odd and even number patterns.
- **Activity 4:** Looking at quantities: Ask the children to record objects when they can see just 1, 2, 3, 4, 5 or any other specified number. Young children may be asked to count a specific type of object. The children could record their findings in a variety of ways, depending on age and ability. Children confident in counting beyond 10 might count and create a tally of the number of cars passing or parked or the number of windows on a street. For children who are working on counting to 10, they could look for and count the number of cars of a given colour, or the number of windows on one house, for example. Ask key questions 5 and 6.

?

KEY QUESTIONS

- 1 Where can you see numbers?
- 2 Are numbers seen on clothing used as decoration, or might they have a use (such as the number on a police officer's jacket)?
- 3 What is the biggest number you can see? Where did you find this?
- 4 What is the smallest number you can see? Where did you find this?
- 5 What was the largest number of objects that you counted? Why do you think there were so many?
- 6 What was the smallest number of objects you counted? Why do you think there were only a few of these?

 ## BACK IN THE CLASSROOM

- Reflect on the Trail with the children , using the photographs taken. Ask them to recall places where they found numbers. Ask their opinions on why numbers are useful. Different groups could share photographs and their records with others.
- Ask the children to consider and recall examples of numbers that they see every day. You might need to start them off with an example, such as 'My bus has a number 6'; 'My house number is 3'.
- Ask the children if they can find and record examples of numbers labelling objects at home.

 **PACKAGING**

*WHAT MATERIALS ARE USED TO PACKAGE A VARIETY OF PRODUCTS
AND WHY HAVE THEY BEEN CHOSEN?*

INTRODUCTION

This Trail aims to investigate the properties of materials in the context of packaging and can be used to enhance science, as well as design and technology topics where children might be designing their own packaging. The children will explore how and why different materials are used to package and advertise a variety of perishable and non-perishable products. This Trail can be followed in a variety of ways to suit your school location and the amenities you have in the locality. Groups of children could visit different shops in a village or town centre, which would reduce the number of children visiting any one shop, or the whole class could visit a supermarket, which would have numerous examples of packaging for a wide range of goods.

CONCEPTS/OBJECTIVES EXPLORED

- Materials can be used in a variety of ways.
- There are similarities and differences between common materials.
- Materials are chosen for specific purposes depending on their properties.
- Knowledge of materials and their properties is useful for making decisions in real life situations.

KEY VOCABULARY

Material
Packaging
Transparent
Translucent
Opaque
Hard
Flexible
Rigid
Insulated
Soft
Card
Plastic
Glass
Mesh
Netting
Paper
Polystyrene foam
Can
Tin
Metal
Aluminium
Bottle
Carton

LOCATION

- Toy shop
- Bakery
- Butcher
- Fishmonger
- Greengrocer
- Hardware shop
- Pharmacy
- Mini supermarket or
- Large supermarket

SCIENTIFIC SKILLS

- Observing
- Collecting data
- Presenting results
- Drawing conclusions based on evidence

INVESTIGATION TYPE

- Exploration
- Survey
- Classification

RESOURCES AND PREPARATION

Each group needs:

Clipboards
Crib sheet or paper
Pens/pencils
Digital cameras

- Discuss with the children: what materials they think are typically used to package different types of products; whether the same materials would be used when packaging a solid, liquid or gas and why they think this.
- Plan a route around your locality, so that you can organise where the groups will go with their adult helpers.
- Either take a copy of the key questions or make a crib sheet for the children and/or adult for use on the Trail.
- Contact the shop(s) you intend to visit to ensure that it is appropriate for you to visit them on your chosen day.

 ON THE TRAIL

WHAT TO DO

In groups:
- Ask the children (in groups, with an adult helper) to visit the following supermarket aisles or shops to take photographs of products and how they are packaged. In each place or shop, ask the children to look closely at how the products are arranged, what colours they can see, and where they have been placed in the shop.
- **Activity 1:** To be repeated in the following locations:
    Fruit and vegetable aisles or a greengrocer
    Fresh meat and fish aisle or butcher/fishmonger
    Cake and bread aisle or bakery
    Toy aisle or toy shop.
- For each example listed, find 3 different examples of packaging (e.g. bag, box and netting):
    Fresh fruits and veg
    Fresh meats and/or fish
    Processed meats and fish
    Bread, cakes and biscuits.
- To support the children's thinking and recording; ask key questions 1 – 7 in each location. Take photographs of the examples selected and record any other useful information such as the amount of packaging used – is there a lot?
- **Activity 2:** To be repeated in the following locations:
    Pharmacy/toiletries aisle or chemist/pharmacy
    Dried/tinned food aisles or mini supermarket
    Household goods aisle or hardware shop.
- Find examples of how gases, liquids and solids are packaged. Are there any examples of products that have 2 states of matter (e.g. a sponge is a solid and gas, fizzy water is a liquid and gas)? To support the children's thinking and recording, ask key questions 1 – 7. Take photographs of the examples selected and record any other useful information as above.

KEY QUESTIONS

- 1 How are the products in this area generally packaged?
- 2 What materials are used to package them? Are they natural or man-made?
- 3 Why have these materials been chosen?
- 4 What property of the packaging material enables you to see the product, or obscures it?
- 5 How has the packaging been designed? What shape is it and why?
- 6 Are there any words or letters on the packaging? Why are these here?
- 7 Does the packaging have any additional information on it? E.g. use by date; nutritional information. Why?

BACK IN THE CLASSROOM

- Discuss what the children saw on their visit. Consider the key information included on the packaging: ingredients, the brand name, food type or product description, use by date, barcode. Ask them why this information is important, e.g. regarding allergies.
- Ask the children to design their own packaging for a product.
- Ask the children to consider how much packaging was used for different products and then specifically for an Easter egg. Is it all necessary? Could less material have been used? Why is using less packaging important? Think about the impact that packaging has on the environment and why it is important to recycle.

Let's Go! SEASHORE SAFARI

SURVIVAL ON THE SEASHORE

ages 5-11

INTRODUCTION

This Trail aims to focus children's attention on the animals that live in a rock pool, exploring where and how they live, and drawing attention to special features that enable rock pool animals to survive in this challenging and constantly changing habitat. Children will be able to notice similarities and differences between rock pool animals and consider how each organism is adapted to its habitat. The children could also discuss how to group the animals that they find, encouraging close observation of features, similarities and differences.

Children will be encouraged to ask questions about the animals they observe (such as how they eat or move or where they are found) and consider how these are affected by the tidal location. They should also consider how this habitat is affected by environmental factors such as weather extremes and plastic pollution.

KEY VOCABULARY

Habitat
Crustaceans
Molluscs
Camouflage
Carnivore
Herbivore
Scavenger
Tides
Adaptation
Pollution
Adaptation

CONCEPTS/OBJECTIVES EXPLORED

- To identify rock pool animals.
- To consider how the animals living in a rock pool are suited to their habitat.
- To note similarities and differences between animals and group them in different ways.
- To consider food chains and food webs and implications of loss of a particular type of organism.
- To consider the effect of human activity such as pollution on the rock pool habitat.

LOCATION

- Rock pools on a rocky shore

SCIENTIFIC SKILLS

- Observing
- Recording
- Collecting data
- Presenting results
- Drawing conclusions based on evidence

INVESTIGATION TYPE

- Exploration
- Survey
- Classification

RESOURCES AND PREPARATION

- Visit the beach beforehand to carry out a risk assessment.
- Check the local tide times and plan your visit to coincide with low tide.
- Contact any interested and supportive parties such as local beach wardens, marine biologists, the National Trust.

Each group needs:

Identification books, laminated ID keys/sheets
White plastic trays
Magnifiers
A waterproof camera
Coloured string and plastic bottle tops

ON THE TRAIL

WHAT TO DO

- On arrival, look at the whole beach and ask the children to look for different types of habitat. (Different states of the tide will affect this.)
- Move onto the beach and stand in an area with rock pools. Ask children to think about how this habitat changes throughout the day due to tides, weather, etc. Ask key question 1. Discuss where to look for and how to handle rock pool animals, replacing overturned rocks. Ask the children to record animals and plants found, taking photographs and noting any observable features. Ask key questions 2 – 4. Discuss how animals observed are suited to living in this habitat, prompted by key question 5.
- When children have had enough time to explore their rock pool and record information, ask key question 6, ensuring that children have an opportunity to consider various ways of grouping the animals and other living organisms in the rock pool. Encourage the children to discuss how the organisms rely on each other (e.g. in food chains or webs) and what might happen if all of one particular organism were removed (e.g. what might happen if all the limpets died?).
- Ask the children to look for any pollution in or around the rock pool and consider how this might affect the animals living in this habitat. Ask key question 7. Give each group a loop of string strung with beads or plastic bottle-tops and ask them to choose the area they would protect. Ask each group to explain why they chose their area to the other groups.
- Provide the children with an opportunity to consider their own questions about the rock pool environment (key question 8) and to find answers to these questions.

KEY QUESTIONS

?

- 1 What animals live in a rock pool and where?
- 2 Where did you find the animals and why do you think they were in that particular place?
- 3 How are these animals /plants adapted to survive on the seashore?
- 4 What happens when the tide goes in/out?
- 5 What characteristics/ features do the animals in a rock pool have?
- 6 How could we group the animals? Why is it useful to classify animals and plants?
- 7 How could we protect seashore habitats better?
- 8 What other questions can we ask about the animals and plants living in a rock pool?

 ## BACK IN THE CLASSROOM

Research:

- Create a fact-file by researching one of the animals seen during the rock pool field study.
- Create a presentation about a chosen animal.
- Look at the Countryside Code and design a 'rock pool code' to encourage visitors to care for the rock pool environment.
- Create observational drawings of animals, seaweeds and shells.
- Create seashore food chains/webs.
- Write 'What am I?' descriptions of animals that live in the rock pools.

Let's Go! SEAWEED

WHAT SEAWEEDS CAN WE FIND ON A BEACH?

ages 6-11

INTRODUCTION

This Trail aims to enable children to explore the features of a beach environment. The children's attention will be drawn to the the variety of living things that populate this environment, in particular seaweeds found along the water (strand) line of a beach. There are many different types of seaweed that could be discovered and, depending on your location, children may be able to find several of these. The children will also be asked to compare similarities and differences between seaweeds and land plants and sort and classify the seaweed. They will be encouraged to raise their own questions and conduct further research back in class. This experience provides opportunity for the children to look closely at a living organism and consider how it can be classified. Children will consider a number of questions in order to draw conclusions about the nature of these living organisms.

CONCEPTS/OBJECTIVES EXPLORED

- To identify wild plants, and consider how seaweed is suited to its habitat, describing the functions of different parts.
- Consider whether seaweed is living, dead or has never been alive.
- Contrast soil-grown plants with seaweed.
- The grouping of living things in different ways.

KEY VOCABULARY

Holdfast

Strand line

Algae (pronounced al'jay or al'gay)

Bryozoa aka 'sea mat' (tiny aquatic invertebrates, typically about 0.5mm long that are found living in colonies on seaweed)

Air sac

LOCATION

- Beach, along the strand line (It is not advisable to pick quantities of living seaweed, e.g. from rock pools)

SCIENTIFIC SKILLS

- Observing
- Recording
- Collecting data
- Presenting results
- Drawing conclusions based on evidence

INVESTIGATION TYPE

- Survey
- Classification

RESOURCES AND PREPARATION

- Discuss hazards of working on a beach, e.g. water, tides, jellyfish, and how to work safely in this environment.
- Ensure that the children have suitable clothing with them, such as waterproof trousers, rubber boots, etc, by sending a letter home to parents/carers.
- Research common seaweed found on shores in this country and show children pictures/photographs/diagrams of these so they can apply their knowledge when out on the Trail. Pre-load images of seaweed and other living things of interest, such as *bryozoa,* onto tablet computers so that they can be used when out and about.
- Purchase common seaweed identification charts, or create your own version of identification keys, for children to use on the Trail.

Each group needs:

Magnifiers
Tablet computers with pre-loaded photographs of seaweed and *Bryozoa*
Identification keys
Pens
Pencils
Paper for recording

ON THE TRAIL

WHAT TO DO

- On arrival at the beach, as a class recap the safe working boundaries and hazards discussed in the classroom.
- **Activity 1:** Ask the children (still in their class group) to observe the features of the environment – the horizon, the sea (whether the tide is in or out, whether it is calm or rough), the strand line (water line), the sand or shingle, any rock pools, living things, or other beach debris. Ask the children to photograph or record these features.
- **Activity 2:** Ask the children to look for different examples of seaweed on the beach and, using a seaweed diagram, identify the following parts of the plant:

    Holdfast

    Stripe

    Float

    Blades

    Midrib

    Receptacle

    Air sacs

- Draw or photograph these parts of the seaweed. Ask the children to label 3 different samples of seaweed if possible. Ask the children to relate the parts they have labelled on the seaweed to the parts of a soil-grown plant, e.g. roots, stem, leaves, flower, etc. Ask key questions 1 – 4.
- **Activity 3:** Model how to create and use a sorting grid so that the children can replicate this to sort their seaweed. Ask the children to look for examples of different seaweeds on the beach and sort these using their grids. If appropriate, place the seaweed samples in the grid; however, do not remove live seaweed from rock pools. As the children are sorting the seaweed, encourage them to raise questions and look closely at the seaweed. Ask key question 4.
- **Activity 4:** Ask the children whether they have noticed anything on the seaweed. Using a magnifier, point out any *bryozoa* (microscopic invertebrate animals) on the seaweed. Ask the children to find their own samples. Gather children back as a class and discuss what the *bryozoa* do. Demonstrate, using the children's fingers, how they filter-feed. Discuss the number of *bryozoa* that are able to fit on a piece of seaweed. Relate the arrays of *bryozoa* on seaweed to children sitting in assembly in a school hall (in rows and columns) – the children could model the *bryozoa* by waving their hands in the air.

KEY QUESTIONS

- 1 Is the seaweed alive or dead?
- 2 Which parts of the seaweed and plants are similar? Which are different?
- 3 Will the seaweed flower?
- 4 Why does some seaweed have air sacs?
- 5 How can you be sure you have sorted the same seaweeds into each group?

 BACK IN THE CLASSROOM

Research:
- Are all seaweeds plants? (Some algae belong to the kingdoms *Chromista*, *Protista* and *Bacteria* rather than *Plantae*).
- Are they fixed in one place like the more familiar plants we see in gardens and parks?
- Is seaweed only found in salt water?
- What different colours of seaweed are there?
- That some types of seaweed have roots and some produce glues.
- Why are there so few algae in the fossil record?
- How fast do seaweeds grow?
- Do all seaweeds photosynthesise?
- Their uses: culinary, medicinal, cosmetic, etc.

Let's Go! SEED DISPERSAL

HOW DO PLANTS DISPERSE THEIR SEEDS?

ages 6-10

INTRODUCTION

This Trail aims to make children aware that different plants produce different kinds of seeds: these differ in their size, shape, number produced and how they can be dispersed. Children will look at observable features of the seeds that they collect. They should begin to question why seeds need to be dispersed and whether seeds can be saved for germinating in the following spring (or at some other time). They will consider how a plant with no apparent seeds is able to reproduce. It is suggested that the Trail is completed in the autumn term, although some examples of seeds can be found throughout the year.

KEY VOCABULARY

Dispersal/disperse
Reproduction/
reproduce
Life cycle
Germination/germinate
Barbs/hooks/sticky
hairs/parachute

CONCEPTS/OBJECTIVES EXPLORED

- Plants need to disperse their seeds to ensure new growth.
- The size of the seed may be related to the size of the plant it produces.
- Seeds can be dispersed by the wind, in water, by animals and through explosions.
- Plants seeds are adapted to ensure that germination occurs where they are dispersed (e.g. some seeds are sealed and only activated by intense heat in forest fires).

LOCATION

- Nearest park/ wood/ nature area
- School grounds
- A place containing a variety of trees and plants

SCIENTIFIC SKILLS

- Observing
- Recording
- Collecting data
- Presenting results
- Drawing conclusions based on evidence

INVESTIGATION TYPE

- Exploration
- Survey
- Classification
- Pattern seeking

RESOURCES AND PREPARATION

- Recap plant reproduction – what is a seed and where are seeds made in the plant?
- If possible, show the BBC documentary 'Private Life of Plants' (narrated by David Attenborough), Episode 1. Discuss with children how seeds are dispersed and what observable clues can be seen on the seed (if any) to establish the method of dispersal. Discuss the purpose of dispersal and consider why some plants aim to disperse their seeds a long distance away from the parent plant, whereas others do not.
- Discuss health and safety with children before going on the Trail:
- Do not eat or taste any of the seeds, fruits or berries found.
- Be aware that some seeds may cause a reaction (and research any local plants that are known to do so, e.g. rose hip).
- Be aware some plants may have barbs or prickly hairs on them.

Each group needs:

Clipboards
Pens
Pencils
Paper
Tablet computers
Magnifying glasses / hand lenses
Collecting bags
Sticky strips
Examples of seed packets

(Other seeds can be collected: for example, popcorn, tomatoes, rice, dried peas, dried beans, strawberries are interesting)

ON THE TRAIL

WHAT TO DO

- Re-emphasise that children should not taste any of the seeds/fruits found whilst on the Trail, that some seeds can cause itching, for example, rose hips and that some seeds have barbs (bristles or sticky hairs).
- Remind the children that they will look closely at the plants in the local environment and will need to decide if they have any observable seeds or fruits.
- **Activity 1:** Ask the children to list the different plants and trees they can see in the environment. Are these a particular type? Explain to the children that they are looking for evidence of seeds and/or fruits that may contain seeds. Most plants will produce seeds at some time during the year and these will germinate into new plants. Children should find several different plants and look for their seeds. These plants may be in different parts of the school grounds or local park/ nature area.
- **Activity 2:** Collect and record the seeds. Ask key question 1. Children can make drawings or use tablet computers to take photographs of these. They may collect the seeds in bags or on sticky-backed plastic to take back into the classroom. Another alternative is to provide a piece of card with a sticky strip on which to collect seeds as the children find them. Are there plants that reproduce by other means (for example, through runners, e.g. strawberries; offsets from bulbs)?
- **Activity 3:** Look for clues as to how seeds are dispersed and consider any specific adaptations (such as hooks or sticky hairs). Ask key questions 2 – 4. Remind the children that seeds can be dispersed by wind, water, on or through an animal, and by explosions. Relate their knowledge and discussions from the 'Preparation' section to what they are seeing out in the field.
- Ensure that that all children wash their hands after handling seeds.

KEY QUESTIONS

- 1 Where are the seeds? Are they inside fruits?
- 2 How do you think the seeds are dispersed?
- 3 Why is it important that seeds are dispersed?
- 4 Can you see new plants growing near the parent plant? Has dispersal been successful?
- 5 Can we keep seeds and germinate them next year?
- 6 How do we need to store the seeds so that we can grow them in the spring?
- 7 What information is on a seed packet that you buy?
- 8 Why should we save seeds? Is it important?

BACK IN THE CLASSROOM

- Look at seeds collected – can the children identify the plant that produces them?
- Looking at the seeds, can we tell how they have been dispersed?
- Ask the children to sort the seeds into different categories. What are these categories?
- Ask the children to consider why some plants produce many seeds whilst others produce few.
- Follow this up with internet research on the seeds of more unusual plants chosen by the children.
- Children could present their findings to the rest of the class.
- Look at a packet of seeds and ask key questions 5 – 8.

Let's Go! SHAPES

WHAT SHAPES CAN WE FIND IN OUR LOCAL PLAY PARK?

ages 3-5

INTRODUCTION

This Trail aims to introduce very young children to shapes that occur in their local environment. Using a local play park for stimulus, the children could apply their knowledge of shape to a real-life situation. This Trail was originally used by a teacher to assess the children's knowledge of shape and then use their experience to create their own junk model of playground equipment. This Trail could also be used to consolidate a unit of work already covered. Depending on what they already know, children could use the Trail to name common shapes, describe their properties and find out about new shapes. They will also have the opportunity to think about and discuss why particular shapes are used for particular things.

CONCEPTS/OBJECTIVES EXPLORED

- To show awareness of similarities of shapes in the environment.
- To show interest in shapes in the environment.
- To begin to use mathematical names for 'solid' 3D shapes and 'flat' 2D shapes, and mathematical terms to describe shapes.
- To select a specific, named shape.
- To explore characteristics of everyday objects and shapes and use mathematical language.

KEY VOCABULARY

Shape
2D
3D
Square
Rectangle
Triangle
Circle
Semi-circle
Hexagon
Octagon
Cube
Cuboid
Sphere
Corners
Sides

LOCATION

- A local play park

SCIENTIFIC SKILLS

- Observing
- Recording
- Collecting data

INVESTIGATION TYPE

- Exploration
- Survey
- Classification

RESOURCES AND PREPARATION

- Enlist the help of several adult helpers to support the journey to and from the play park, and to assist you with the activities on the Trail.
- Ensure that the children have some understanding of 'flat' shapes so that they know what they are looking for on the Trail and describe or discuss the features of a square, rectangle, circle and triangle before starting.
- If appropriate, also describe and discuss 3D shapes with the children.
- Visit the play park so that you can pre-plan your route to and from this location, and have an idea of the shapes that the children are likely to see.

Each group needs:

Digital cameras

Clipboards

Pens/pencils

Assessment proforma sheet for adults

A selection of flat shapes or labels

A selection of 3D shapes or labels

ON THE TRAIL

WHAT TO DO

- When they arrive at the play park, ask the children to look around them and, without saying the shape name out loud, identify a shape that they can name.
- Ask the children to go and stand next to a shape that they can name. An adult helper should go to each child and ask him/her to whisper the name of the shape they are standing by. Ask the adult helper to record this on a proforma or assessment sheet.
- Repeat this activity for different shapes in the play park.
- Ask the children to collect a flat shape or label to represent the shape they have found in the play park and take a photograph of this with the label/flat shape in the picture. Use the adults assisting you to support this.
- Gather the children around you. Say that you are going to count to 3 and then ask them to stand next to a piece of equipment that has the following shape in it:

    Square

- Gather them around you again and repeat this activity for the following shapes:

    Rectangle

    Circle

    Triangle

- Record each shape that they stand next to in groups, using the digital camera.
- Ask the children to find a different example of the same shapes above and photograph them. Collect as many examples as you can of the 4 basic shapes.
- Ask the children to find examples of other shapes (not yet named), e.g. hexagon or semi-circle, and ask if the children know what these are called. Photograph these new shapes in the environment with their labels/flat shape equivalents alongside.
- Extend the activity above to include 3D shapes if appropriate.
- Ask the key questions throughout the Trail to encourage the children to think about the properties of the shapes they are seeing and to think about why they have been used.

KEY QUESTIONS

- 1 What shapes can you see?
- 2 How many sides does the shape have?
- 3 How many corners does the shape have?
- 4 How do you know it is a ...?
- 5 What can you tell me about...?
- 6 Why has that shape been used?
- 7 Why hasn't a ... been used instead?

BACK IN THE CLASSROOM

- Recap shape names and properties using the photographs you have taken to support the discussion. How do shapes look in a photograph compared with real life, e.g. 2D, 3D, and why is this?
- What were the children's favourite shapes and why? What new shape names did they learn?
- Ask the children to use their knowledge of shape in the play park to design and create their own playgrounds using junk modelling. Discuss with them why they are using particular shapes for their equipment. Use this activity as a way of assessing their knowledge about shape.

INTRODUCTION

This Trail aims to create an engaging context for investigating materials, in particular those used to make shoes. This is based on the story 'Centipede's 100 Shoes' by Tony Ross. Although suited to younger children, the problem can be adapted to suit other age groups using other stories. The children are presented with the problem: Which shoes would have been the best ones for the centipede to buy? The Trail encourages children to consider choices to be made when purchasing shoes. They will consider and describe the function of shoes in order to link a material and its properties. In choosing the most suitable, they will discuss and compare properties of different shoes: whether they are easy for a centipede to tie, are waterproof, durable and flexible; whether colour is important; and if the shoes seem good value for money, given the centipede's need for so many.

KEY VOCABULARY

Materials
Properties
Durability
Flexibility
Waterproof
Suitability of materials
Function of materials
Ease (of putting on)
Centipede
Legs
Number
Habitat
Pairs

CONCEPTS/OBJECTIVES EXPLORED

- Everyday materials can be compared and grouped according to their properties.
- Knowledge of materials and their properties is useful for making decisions in real-life situations.

LOCATION

- Shoe shop(s)

SCIENTIFIC SKILLS

- Observing
- Recording
- Collecting data
- Drawing conclusions based on evidence

INVESTIGATION TYPE

- Exploration
- Survey
- Classification

RESOURCES AND PREPARATION

Each group needs:

Lots of adult support
Digital cameras

- Children will need to have read at least some of the chosen story text providing the 'real-life' shoe problem.
- It would be useful for children to have tested some shoes or materials, e.g. the easiest to do up, most flexible, and to have considered the key vocabulary list.
- Approach the shop(s) you intend to visit beforehand, to seek permission to take a class. Some shops may require a letter explaining the purpose of the Trail and what their role would be; prepare well in advance of the trip.
- Ensure that you visit shop(s) that sell shoes for different purposes, e.g. fashion, outdoor pursuits, budget, luxury.
- Ask the children to write down a list of criteria about their 'ideal' shoes so that they can take this with them on the Trail.

ON THE TRAIL

WHAT TO DO

On the Trail, the children should:

- Visit one or more shops. In each shop, the children should listen to a welcome/health and safety talk about behaviour in the shop. They need to be aware of other customers, not touching the goods on sale and generally conducting themselves with care and respect. Ideally this talk should be given by one of the staff in the shop, but it could be led by the teacher or other adult with the group/class.
- Work in small groups to look around at the different shoes that are for sale. The children should refer to the list of criteria that they have brought with them. Encourage the children to imagine the character for whom they are choosing the shoes and consider what this character would be looking for. Ask key questions 1 – 7.
- Discuss how changes in an environment or in the seasons might affect what kind of shoes are selected.
- Observe and think about how the shoes have been grouped in the shop. Ask the children why the shoes have been arranged in this way.
- Make a shortlist of three possible pairs of shoes that would fit their criteria for the centipede (or other fictitious character).
- Take photographs of each one of the shortlisted shoes.
- Photograph or record the price of the shoes.
- Discuss whether the children think that the shoes offer good value for money, considering the amount and type of material used. Is there a correlation between material and cost?. The shop staff might be happy to assist with these discussions. Ask the shop staff if they would calculate the cost of 21 pairs of shoes for the centipede (or another story character). Ask the children to decide which shoes they think are most suitable for purchase. Either photograph or record the shoes that have been chosen.

KEY QUESTIONS

- 1 What materials have been used to make the shoes? Why were they chosen?
- 2 How many different materials have been used to make these shoes?
- 3 Are the materials used man-made or natural?
- 4 Which shoes are likely to be: the most durable; waterproof; protective?
- 5 Which shoes are the most flexible? Is this important?
- 6 Which shoes are suited to their purpose? How do you know this?
- 7 How are shoes advertised or promoted by the shop?

BACK IN THE CLASSROOM

- Ask the children to share their findings about shoes that were best for the character in the story.
- The 'Centipede's 100 Shoes' story offers lots of rich experiences in investigating numbers, pairs, odd and even numbers. The children could further investigate centipede facts.
- Create paper centipedes using the fact that each must have 1 pair of legs per body segment and an odd number of body segments. Explore the mathematical relationships between body segments and legs.
- The children could investigate where centipedes are found, whether they are carnivores or herbivores and their life cycle.

Let's Go! SPEED

HOW FAST DO OBJECTS AND PEOPLE TRAVEL IN OUR LOCAL AREA?

ages 7-11

INTRODUCTION

This Trail aims for children to explore the concept of speed and how it is measured. Calculating the speed of something involves two units: time and distance. It is important for children to have practical experience of this measure using real-life examples. This Trail will deepen children's appreciation of speed, providing an opportunity to make quantitative observations. Children should extend their qualitative observations (it is fast or slow-moving) into more explicit results using the data they collect. This Trail will also enable children to ask questions about speed and test out their ideas. For example, do all pedestrians walk at an average of 4 miles per hour (mph)? They will explore factors that might affect walking speed, such as age, pushing a buggy or carrying heavy shopping. This is an opportunity for children to take measurements, consider appropriate units and use these.

CONCEPTS/OBJECTIVES EXPLORED

- To understand the concept of speed.
- To estimate and read time with increasing accuracy.
- To measure length with increasing accuracy.
- To use data to make calculations of speed.

KEY VOCABULARY

Speed
Distance
Time
Second
Metre
Fast
Faster
Fastest
Slow
Slower
Slowest
Decimal
Metres per second
Miles per hour
Kilometres per hour
Length

LOCATION

- Any location where groups of 4 children can mark out a 10m stretch without causing a hazard or blocking a pavement: a long pavement or road

SCIENTIFIC SKILLS

- Observing
- Measuring
- Recording
- Collecting data
- Presenting results
- Drawing conclusions based on evidence

INVESTIGATION TYPE

- Exploration
- Survey

RESOURCES AND PREPARATION

- Visit your local area to find the best place to do the Trail with children, thinking about optimum time of day and how much traffic will be there (on both the road and the pavement).
- Enlist the assistance of adult helpers, both to walk the children to and from the Trail destination, and also to assist them when they are there.
- Discuss the meaning of speed and how it can be measured.
- Explain how to calculate speed by measuring the distance covered in a certain time. This could be practised in the school playground with children walking/running a given distance (e.g. between 2 cones) and recording how long this takes.

Each group needs:

Digital cameras
Stopwatches
Trundle wheel
Cones
Chalk
Metre stick
Clipboards
Paper or proforma
to record on
Pens/pencils

ON THE TRAIL

WHAT TO DO

- On the journey to your destination, look for signs in the area that relate to speed, such as speed limits or traffic calming initiatives. Ask key questions 1 – 3. Take photographs of these as well as where they are placed, to discuss back in the classroom.
- At your chosen location, use the trundle wheel to mark out a distance of 20m on the pavement (out of the way of pedestrians) and put the cones at each end of this distance to mark. Ask the children to predict the time that a motor vehicle will take to pass between the cones (do they think it will be 1s, 2s, 10s, 1 minute, etc.). You can show them that it is almost impossible to measure this accurately if the car is travelling close to the speed limit of 30mph because this is 13m/s, so it takes only 1.5s to pass the cones (without taking into consideration reaction times).
- Ask the children to time how long it takes for them to walk the same distance. Calculate the children's speed: distance ÷ time = 20m ÷ time taken. Compare the children's walking speed to the motor vehicle speed.
- Encourage the children to think of the following:

    Something that moves slower than a motor vehicle but faster than they walk

    Something that moves slower than they walk

    Something that moves faster than a motor vehicle.
- Ask the children to set up a course with cones and observe pedestrians walking by. The children could measure the time taken for the pedestrians to walk 20m between cones and calculate their speed. Ask key questions 4 – 7.

?

KEY QUESTIONS

- 1 What is the speed limit of the road?
- 2 Did all the cars travel at the same speed? Why do you think this was?
- 3 Did you see a pattern in the vehicle type and speed it travelled (e.g. bicycle compared to car)?
- 4 How fast did people walk?
- 5 Is this the same for all people?
- 6 Who was the fastest/slowest person you recorded?
- 7 What factors might have affected how quickly someone was walking?

BACK IN THE CLASSROOM

- Consider calculating speeds for other living things, e.g. how quickly do snails move or how quickly does a plant grow?
- Look at common phrases or sayings involving speed, such as 'quick as a flash', 'in the blink of an eye', 'spreading like wild fire' or 'at the drop of a hat' and ask the children to research the speeds actually involved in these sayings.
- Look at why speed limits are in place for cars. Why is the speed limit 20 or 30mph in built-up areas? Where are the safest roads?

INTRODUCTION

This Trail aims to get children to observe and identify the changes that happen in their local area in spring. Unlike the 'Seasonal Changes' Trail (found in 'Let's Go! Science Trails'), which is a longitudinal study, repeated throughout the year, this Trail can be completed in isolation, focusing on changes that happen in spring. This Trail was trialled as part of a topic on 'Space', where the children were looking at the position of the Earth and how this causes seasons. However, this Trail would fit into a number of topic themes, such as 'Changes'. This is a child-led Trail, where the children decide what evidence they are going to collect and how they will record their findings. What are the differences compared to winter, summer or autumn?

KEY VOCABULARY

Spring
Season
Precipitation
Temperature
Light levels
Clocks changing
Daffodil
Tulip
Bees
Insects
Birds

CONCEPTS/OBJECTIVES EXPLORED

- Environments are affected by changes in season.
- Animals and plants that live in a particular environment are affected by seasonal changes.
- To observe and identify common plants and animals that live in my local area.
- That spring is a time of year when new life often occurs.

LOCATION

- A Royal Horticultural Society (RHS) garden, one of the RHS partner gardens or any similar organisation's garden near your location
- A local public garden or park

SCIENTIFIC SKILLS

- Observing
- Recording
- Collecting data
- Drawing conclusions based on evidence
- Choosing a scientific approach to use

INVESTIGATION TYPE

- Exploration
- Survey
- Changes over time

RESOURCES AND PREPARATION

- A public garden location should be chosen if possible, as it is likely to be rich in a variety of flora and fauna; alternatively, a local park could be visited.
- Children will need to have a thorough understanding of winter so they can compare and contrast observations made on the Trail.
- Discuss what the children will be wearing on the day of the Trail and why. How are clothing choices affected by seasonal changes? What would they predict that other people will wear outdoors at this time of year?
- As the Trail is child-led, ask the children to plan what they want to find out, and decide what evidence they want to collect. How will they convince others that spring has definitely arrived?

Each group needs:

Digital cameras

Tablet computers with identification apps which can also be used as additional cameras

Identification keys for flowers, trees, plants and insects

Hand lenses

Data loggers might be useful

ON THE TRAIL

WHAT TO DO

- On arrival at your location, observe the weather and other environmental factors. What are the light levels? What is the weather? Is it sunny or misty? Is there dew on the grass? Has water gathered in places indicating that it has rained? What is the temperature? Can children 'see their breath'? Ask key questions 1 – 4.
- Observe what people are wearing: Is this likely to be different to other seasons – gloves, hats, scarves and outerwear? Look at people's shoes– are they open or closed? Are they waterproof? Why have these choices been made? Were the children's predictions correct about what people would be wearing? These questions are simply to challenge the children's thinking about whether these sorts of clues can accurately determine the season.
- In small groups, walk around the garden taking photographs and recording the following:
- Look at trees, bedding plants, bushes and shrubs. What evidence is there that plants are starting to grow (e.g. buds or blossom)?
- Are there plants growing on walls, or through cracks in the paving?
- Look closely at the flowers. Are any insects present (e.g. bees)? Complete a tally chart of the different insects seen.
- Ask key question 5. Complete a tally chart of the different colours/flower species/common plants that the children can see.
- Can the children see evidence of other animals preparing for the warmer weather (e.g. birds building nests)? Ask key question 6 and ask the children to complete a tally chart.
- Ask key questions 7 and 8. Can the children find any other evidence that spring has arrived?
- Ask the children to follow their planned investigations and find and record the evidence they need to confirm that spring has arrived.

KEY QUESTIONS

- 1 What are the main changes in weather that indicate it is spring?
- 2 What other changes occur in spring? Clocks are moved forward, sun is higher in the sky, days are longer, etc.
- 3 How would this change affect the wildlife you can see?
- 4 How would this change affect what clothing and shoes are worn?
- 5 What was the most common flower seen (e.g. by colour/type/species)?
- 6 What was the most common insect seen (e.g. by species/feature such as wings)?
- 7 Why do you think many animals give birth to their young in springtime?
- 8 Why are you likely to see more animals in the spring? Likewise plants?

BACK IN THE CLASSROOM

- Activities directly related to the Trail you have been on: if not all the ON THE TRAIL activities were undertaken, spend time in the classroom doing the remainder. Could be a series of bullet points or text (or a mix). Instructional writing.
- Children could complete an activity to convince an alien that it is spring. What evidence did they find to confirm this? Ideas could be shared in reports, posters, etc.
- Create graphs from the tally charts generated on the Trail.
- Discuss differences in light levels, the Sun's position in the sky, temperature, precipitation, etc. Relate the light levels and the Sun's position to the Earth's position on its axis and its orbital position in spring. Can the children find data on average rainfall, temperature, hours of sunlight, etc. to support their findings?

Let's Go! STEM IN ACTION

ages 6-11

INTRODUCTION

This Trail aims to encourage children to appreciate the impact and uses of science, technology, engineering and maths in their local area. This Trail was inspired by the work of Natasha Serret, a leading proponent of outdoor learning, who completed a similar activity with secondary school children. This Trail is an excellent introduction to STEM subjects, as it allows children to explore these as discrete subjects whilst appreciating how they are intrinsically linked. It is also an opportunity for children to appreciate that everything that they see created by people has been imagined; the designer had a vision of what was needed, be it a new material, structure or concept and that all human innovation is incredible.

CONCEPTS/OBJECTIVES EXPLORED

- To see scientific concepts demonstrated in the outdoors.
- To see technology and technological advancements outdoors.
- To see examples of engineering and how it is used in everyday life.
- To see mathematical concepts demonstrated in the outdoors.

KEY VOCABULARY

Science
Scientific
Technology
Technological
Engineering
Engineered
Maths
Mathematical
Discipline
Subject
Biology
Chemistry
Physics
Number
Shape
Space
Data

LOCATION

- Any location, including the school playground

SCIENTIFIC SKILLS

- Observing
- Recording
- Collecting data
- Presenting results
- Drawing conclusions based on evidence

INVESTIGATION TYPE

- Survey
- Classification

RESOURCES AND PREPARATION

Each group needs:

Digital cameras
Crib sheets with key
questions on them
Clipboards
Pens/pencils

- Brainstorm with your class their thoughts on science, technology, engineering and maths. Ask them to predict examples of the applications of these subjects that they might see outdoors. Consider whether the children see the subjects in isolation or already see links.

- If you plan to visit an area where the children may become an obstruction, e.g. in a busy high street, prepare well beforehand to ensure that you choose somewhere suitable for them to stand.

- Practise 'making a frame' with your hands before going on the Trail: make the thumbs and forefingers on both hands into an 'L' shape and join them together.

 ## ON THE TRAIL

WHAT TO DO

- Ask the children to look closely at the area they are in, spending several minutes on this activity. How much have they noticed? What is happening?

- Explain that they will need to find the very best example (in their opinion) of each of the following: something scientific; something technological; something that has been engineered and something mathematical. Re-cap what these terms mean (based on the work you did in preparation for the Trail).

- Organise the children to work in pairs. Remind them all how to make the frame with their hands. They will be using this frame to 'capture' lots of examples of the STEM subjects in action, by completing the following activities:

- **Activity 1:** Find examples of science in action. Encourage the children to 'frame' a number of ideas with their hands, discussing each one with their partner. Use key questions 1 – 3 to aid their discussion. They must reach agreement on the best example from all those considered (and for older children, they should justify their choice) and take a photograph of this example.

- **Activity 2:** As above, but this time the focus is technology. Encourage the children to find several examples, using key question 3 to support the discussion. The children must take a photograph of the best example.

- **Activity 3:** As above, but the focus is on engineering or something that solves a problem. Encourage the children to frame a number of examples, using key questions 4 – 6 to discuss their ideas and photograph their agreed best example.

- **Activity 4:** The focus will be maths. Ask the pairs to discuss why what they are framing is mathematical and agree their choice, before photographing. Ask key question 7.

- **Activity 5:** Challenge the children to find and frame examples that encompass as many of the STEM subjects as possible. Discuss which example is the best demonstration of STEM subjects working together and photograph this. How do the STEM subjects work together in the area they are? Ask children to select the photograph they feel is the most boring/interesting from all the examples. Why do they feel this way?

KEY QUESTIONS

- 1 Why is your choice scientific?
- 2 What subject discipline might apply (e.g. biology, chemistry or physics – for younger children simply consider this as a way of explaining the world around us)? Is there more than one?
- 3 Why is your choice technological? How does this work?
- 4 Why does your choice represent engineering?
- 5 What problem is being solved?
- 6 What would happen in our world without this example of engineering?
- 7 What area of maths can you find e.g. number, shape, symmetry, data, time, etc.? Is there more than one?

 BACK IN THE CLASSROOM

- Look at the photographs taken and share these as a class, with each pair presenting and explaining their chosen examples. This activity provides a good assessment opportunity, as the children will need to draw on their knowledge of science, technology, engineering and maths in justifying their choices.
- Look at the last photograph taken and ask: can you isolate the STEM subjects in the pictures already taken, or are they all there in one form or another? Children should discuss this in their pairs, looking back through the photographs that they took of the STEM subjects in the first 4 activities.

Let's Go! SUGAR

HOW MUCH SUGAR IS IN THE FOODS WE EAT REGULARLY?

ages 7-11

INTRODUCTION

This Trail aims for children to become more aware of how much sugar is in food, especially foods where this is less obvious. They will consider the impact of eating too much sugar on health and well-being. This Trail might be used as part of a healthy lifestyle topic, or during any topic about food. The best location to use is a large supermarket, where the children can visit different aisles in groups, with an adult helper to support their learning. The children will look at a variety of everyday foods, including those in boxes and packets, tins and jars. They will look at different food groups such as cereals, dairy products and confectionery, providing a wide range of products to compare and contrast. The Trail will also be used to highlight the different words used for sugar and demonstrate the importance of reading food labels when making food choices.

KEY VOCABULARY

Healthy eating
Sugar
Sucrose
Maltose
Dextrose
Fructose
Glucose
Galactose
Lactose
High fructose corn syrup
Glucose solids
Cane juice
Dehydrated cane juice
Cane juice solids
Dextrin
Dextran
Maltodextrin
Barley malt
Corn syrup
Corn syrup solids
Diatase
Ethyl maltol
Beet sugar

CONCEPTS/OBJECTIVES EXPLORED

- That sugar is a carbohydrate and provides the body with energy.
- That sugar can be part of a healthy diet.
- That 'free' or 'added sugar' is to be avoided.
- To read food labels correctly and understand the sugar content of foods.

LOCATION

- A large supermarket

SCIENTIFIC SKILLS

- Observing
- Measuring
- Recording
- Collecting data
- Presenting results
- Drawing conclusions based on evidence

INVESTIGATION TYPE

- Exploration
- Survey
- Classification

RESOURCES AND PREPARATION

- Contact the supermarket that you intend to visit to ensure that the date and time planned is mutually convenient.
- Check out the supermarket in advance of the visit so that you can plan a route for the groups, directing adult helpers and groups to specific aisles when looking for products.
- Discuss labelling on products. The first ingredient listed is the largest component of the product. Also discuss all the different names for sugar as they appear in food (there are around 60 in use).
- Discuss recommended daily intake for sugar: children between the ages of 4 and 8 should have no more than 3 teaspoons or 19g a day; 24g for 7-10 year-olds and 30g for adults. Ask the children to predict what they think they have daily and record this prediction.

Each group needs:

Clipboard
Paper or prepared crib sheet
Pens/pencils
Digital cameras
Cards with daily recommended intake amount on for reminders or traffic light cards, e.g.:

- green — low sugar content per 100g for children
- amber/orange — medium sugar content per 100g for children
- red — high sugar content per 100g for children

 ON THE TRAIL

WHAT TO DO

- For each of the activities, it is really important that children read the correct nutritional information. This is rarely on the front of the package, which usually lists information for a standard portion. Demonstrate to the class (and adult helpers) where they need to look for information about sugar. There are usually two columns, one specifically listing food group amounts, vitamins and minerals per 100g. Sugars are usually listed under 'carbohydrates'. Look at a range of labels on different packages together, to ensure that the children collect the required information.
- **Activity 1:** For each of the products listed below (or choose a selection of your own), ask the children to choose 3 different varieties/brands. For each, photograph the product, ingredient list and nutritional information. Ask key questions 1 and 2.
- **Activity 2:** Identify and record the amount of sugar per 100g that is in each product selected, e.g.:

    Ready meal 1 — toad in the hole — 23g sugar per 100g

    Ready meal 2 — chicken korma — 50g sugar per 100g

    Ready meal 3 — carbonara — 38g sugar per 100g.

- **Activity 3:** Read the ingredients list on the chosen products and look for words that mean that sugar is present, e.g. dextrose. Note the position of sugar in the list, e.g. 5th.
- **Activity 4:** Ask children in your group to predict and note down the product in the aisle that they think contains the largest amount of sugar. Ask the children to check their predictions. Repeat for the product that has the least amount of sugar.
- **Activity 5:** Work out the number of teaspoons per 100g of each product in the list below using this approximate guide: 1 teaspoon is approximately 4 grams. Order the products found by quantity of sugar per 100g. Ask key questions 3 – 7.
- Repeat the activity for the next set of products in a new aisle.

Suggested products:

A ready meal	Frozen potato products
A litre of fizzy drink	Chocolate
Jar of cook-in sauce (e.g. bolognaise or curry)	Fruit juice
Ham	Yogurt
Fish fingers	Cereal

?

KEY QUESTIONS

- 1 Which products from the list do you think will contain little or no sugar?
- 2 Which products from the list do you think will contain a lot of sugar?
- 3 Which product did you find that had the largest amount of sugar per 100g?
- 4 Which product did you find that had the least amount of sugar per 100g?
- 5 Were you surprised by any of your findings?
- 6 How easy was it to find the sugar content on the food labels?
- 7 Do you think food labelling could be made clearer? How?

BACK IN THE CLASSROOM

- Share and discuss what the children found out. Were there any surprises? How easy was it to predict sugar content? Ask children to weigh out sugar content for various drinks to help others visualise this.
- Research sugar content for foods that were not packaged, or had no nutritional information on them, e.g. fruit and vegetables, store-baked bread, fresh meat or fish.
- Discuss/research why eating a piece of fruit is better than drinking juice? Consider the impact of sugar on healthy eating.
- Discuss the health implications for eating too much added sugar — what are the effects of sugar on the body?

Let's Go! TESSELLATION

WHERE CAN WE SEE TESSELLATION USED IN THE WORLD AROUND US?

INTRODUCTION

This Trail aims to help children to understand the concept of tessellation using real-life contexts. The children will identify what shapes are often used, e.g. triangles, rectangles, etc. and how they are reflected, rotated or translated to make tessellations. Children might also discuss congruence. The children will observe how tessellated shapes are used in a variety of ways, e.g. on walls, flooring or for decorative purposes (e.g. on fabrics). This Trail will also give children the opportunity to use vocabulary associated with shape work, apply what they already know and will provide opportunities to extend this knowledge further. One location may be used for this Trail; alternatively, compare and contrast a number of locations so that children can see how tessellation is used in a range of contexts.

CONCEPTS/OBJECTIVES EXPLORED

- To name common 2D shapes.
- To describe properties of shape, including number of sides.
- To understand what tessellation is.
- To understand how shapes are tessellated through reflection, rotation or translation.

KEY VOCABULARY

Tessellation
Congruent
Rotation
Symmetry
Translation
Shape
Polygon
Reflection
Mirror image

LOCATION

- Church
- Other location where tessellations are present

SCIENTIFIC SKILLS
- Observing
- Recording
- Collecting data

INVESTIGATION TYPE
- Exploration
- Survey
- Classification

RESOURCES AND PREPARATION

Each group needs:

Digital cameras
Tablet computers
Clipboards
Paper/proforma sheet
Pens/pencils
Key vocabulary on cards/
laminated sheets

- Introduce children to any key vocabulary before they go so that it can be used. Depending on the age and ability of the children, ensure that they know the names of and can identify common 2D shapes, and the words tessellate, congruent, polygon, symmetry, etc.
- Check out place(s) you intend to visit and the planned route in advance, gaining any necessary permissions (if needed). It is also useful to take photographs of the places/locations for your own reference; the children could also be shown these prior to going on the Trail and asked to find examples for themselves.

 ON THE TRAIL

WHAT TO DO

- On the way to your chosen location, ask the children to identify and name any shapes that they recognise (both 2D and 3D). They could complete a tally chart of them. Also ask them if they notice any patterns that use shapes or tessellations on the journey.
- At your location, arrange the children in smaller groups.
- **Activity 1:** Ask the children to find examples of two different tessellations and record these, using a digital camera or by drawing them. Depending on the age of the children, ask some or all of key questions 1 – 4.
- **Activity 2:** Bring the class back together. Point out any new vocabulary or concepts that you would like the children to use or identify whilst on the Trail, e.g. congruence. Use vocabulary cards to show the children each new word and then point out examples in your location.
- **Activity 3:** Hand out vocabulary cards to the groups of children (between 5 and 10 cards should be sufficient for each group, depending on the number of locations planned and the time you are able to spend on the Trail). Some sample vocabulary is listed below. You may wish to use these words or select your own. Ask the children to find examples, place the vocabulary cards alongside these and take photographs.

Triangle	Translation
Square	Right angle
Rectangle	Acute angle
Hexagon	Obtuse angle
Other common 2D shapes	Congruent
Symmetry	Regular
Reflection	Irregular
Rotation	

KEY QUESTIONS

- 1 What shape or shapes make up the tessellated pattern that you can see?
- 2 What are the properties of those shapes — how many sides, edges, corners, etc.?
- 3 Are the shapes regular or irregular?
- 4 How many different shapes can you see in your tessellated pattern?
- 5 What shapes have been used to make the building?
- 6 What shape is the floor? The walls? The doors and windows? The roof?
- 7 Why have those shapes been chosen?
- 8 How do those shapes support the building?

 BACK IN THE CLASSROOM

- Look at the photographs that each group took and look for similarities or differences in the shapes/ tessellations that were recorded. Does everyone agree that the examples photographed exemplify the words on the vocabulary cards?
- Make your own tessellated patterns using regular and irregular shapes, using the Trail as inspiration.
- Create your own building from a variety of materials (wooden, Lego or Duplo bricks, stickle bricks, or drinking straws, etc.), using the structures and shapes seen. Decorate it with tessellated patterns for the floor or walls.
- Research 3D tessellations and where these are found, e.g. on a football.

Let's Go! TRAIN STATIONS

HOW BUSY IS OUR LOCAL TRAIN STATION?

ages 9-11

INTRODUCTION

This Trail aims for children to work with a range of mathematical themes and apply these in a relevant context, at a train station. It is also a really good experience for children to visit one, as at some point in their lives they are likely to travel by train. Familiarity with accessing and applying information in the station itself can help children to make sense of these sometimes apparently abstract concepts. The children could also look at the potential risks or dangers of a station environment and offer suggestions as to how to reduce these. The children will look at how busy their local station is and compare and contrast it to other stations, depending on whether they live in a rural or urban location. The children will gather a variety of data at the station and use these data to draw conclusions.

KEY VOCABULARY

Time
Measure
Calculation
Safety
Signs
Timetable
Hours
Minutes
Length
Metres
Data
Train
Tube
Bridge
Barrier

CONCEPTS/OBJECTIVES EXPLORED

- To read, write and convert time between analogue and digital 12- and 24-hour clocks.
- To solve problems involving conversion from hours to minutes; minutes to seconds; years to months; weeks to days.
- To interpret and present discrete and continuous data using appropriate graphical methods, including bar charts and time graphs.
- To measure length in context.

LOCATION

- A train or tube station

SCIENTIFIC SKILLS

- Observing
- Measuring
- Recording
- Collecting data
- Presenting results

INVESTIGATION TYPE

- Exploration
- Survey

RESOURCES AND PREPARATION

- Before you take children out, visit your local station and check with the station manager the best time to bring children.
- Enlist plenty of adult support to ensure that appropriate child:adult ratios are met and the risks reduced.
- In order to give the children a context of what is busy or not: research which train stations are the busiest/quietest both in this country and in other places. What are their maximum capacities? How many passengers/trains use them daily/monthly or annually?
- Look at different types of trains – overground, underground, freight, passenger, etc. and how these are powered. Look at whether they use live train tracks, overhead electrical wires or diesel. Investigate the amount of electricity that may be needed. Discuss electrical safety.

Each group needs:

Digital cameras

Measuring wheel or measuring app – e.g. Smart Measure

Tablet computer to record data

Chalk to mark front and back of train

ON THE TRAIL

WHAT TO DO

- On the approach to the station, look at the features: does it have a car park, taxi rank, bus stop, bike rack, etc.? What signs direct you to the correct place? How do people get to the train station? Is it in a town centre or residential area? Does it have a bridge or barrier across a road? Why would this be here? Ask the children to take photographs of these features. Can they predict how busy their train station is using these clues?
- If there is a barrier, observe how it works: pulleys, warning sounds, levers, etc. Wait for the barrier lights to flash and time how long it takes the train to arrive after the barrier has been lowered.
- Inside the station, identify the different areas – ticket hall/machines, stairs or escalators, entrance to the platform, barriers etc. Ask key question 1. Ask the children to count the number of people here (if possible). Can they see any other maths here (e.g. shapes, timetables, chip and pin or cash machines etc.)?
- Go onto the platform. Ask the children to identify the features (including any safety ones) of the platform. Ask key questions 2 – 5. Take photographs of these features.
- Ask the children to measure the length of the platform with a trundle wheel, or by using an app on a tablet computer (there are several available).
- Ask the children to record what types of train pass through the station – are they local, national, tube trains or freight trains? What is the length of each train (number of carriages)?
- Look at the destination of the trains as they approach. Ask key question 6. Look at the train timetables (if available) and check if the trains run on time. Does the timetable give specific times of when the train will arrive, or is it 'every … minutes'?
- Record the number of trains passing through the station in an hour. Ask key questions 7 – 8. Do the trains look empty or full? Estimate how many people could travel on the train? Measure the length of time that trains stop at the platform.

KEY QUESTIONS

- 1 What information is available for passengers – how is this displayed?
- 2 Can you see any warning signs or markings?
- 3 What are the warnings and why are these here?
- 4 What other information is available on the platform and where is this?
- 5 How are passengers alerted to incoming or departing trains?
- 6 Are they travelling north, south, east or west?
- 7 How many trains stop at the station? How many do not?
- 8 How many people get on or off?

 ## BACK IN THE CLASSROOM

- Use measurements of trains and lengths of platforms to work out whether there is a link between the length of the trains and the length of the platform. Using this information, how many trains could be at the station at one time?
- Calculate how long the journey is to the next station and between stations both locally and further afield, using the timetables.
- Use the data and evidence collected to create graphs – number of passengers in an hour, number of trains, how many trains stopped/did not? Answer the question: how busy is our local station?

Let's Go! TRANSPORT

COUNTING, RECORDING AND ORDERING NUMBERS:
A MATHS TRAIL ABOUT VEHICLES

ages 4-7

INTRODUCTION

This Trail aims for children to explore the local environment, with an emphasis on the roads and a local railway bridge. They will recognise and record numbers that they see on trains, buses, cars and lorries and count these. Children will conduct a local traffic survey, counting and recording the different colours and types of transport they see passing them. They will also go to a local railway bridge and use their senses to listen, look and feel the trains travelling beneath them. They will observe warning signs and notices on the roads and around the railway. Children will also be asked about the science that they see while they are out. They will consider the materials used for rails and roads and the way that various vehicles move.

CONCEPTS/OBJECTIVES EXPLORED

- To count to ten and beyond in order to complete a survey.
- To recognise digits 1 – 9.
- To look at objects and observe similarities and differences, patterns and changes.
- To find out and identify features of objects and events.

KEY VOCABULARY

Natural
Man-made
Car
Lorry
Motorbike
Bicycle
Bus
Train
Railway barrier
Railway bridge
Railway station

LOCATION

- Main road
- Railway barrier, bridge or station, or all 3

SCIENTIFIC SKILLS

- Observing
- Measuring
- Recording
- Collecting data
- Presenting results
- Drawing conclusions based on evidence

INVESTIGATION TYPE

- Exploration
- Survey
- Classification
- Pattern seeking

RESOURCES AND PREPARATION

Each group needs:

Digital cameras
Tablet computer
Sound buttons
Clicker
Pencils
First aid kit
Clipboards

- The most important preparation for this Trail is to ensure that you have enough adult support as the children are very young. The teacher who originally conducted this Trail with his Reception class enlisted support for an adult to child ratio of 1:2. For older children, the adult:child ratio could be less.

- Walk the route you intend to take beforehand and take photographs for your own reference. Record traffic lights changing and barriers going up and down in case this fails on the actual Trail.

- Review train timetables so you know that the children will see trains, either at a barrier, on a bridge or at a station. If going to a station, request permission to bring children and find out the best time to do so.

ON THE TRAIL

WHAT TO DO

- Divide the class into two equal groups. One group will investigate the railway bridge, station or barrier first, the other will conduct the traffic survey. 30 to 40 minutes is a good amount of time to spend on each activity.

Activity 1:

- On the way to the railway bridge, barrier or station, ask the children to name the different types of vehicle they see on the way, recording these through photographs.

- At the railway bridge, barrier or station, ask the children to explain its purpose and function. What materials have been used to make it? What warning signs are there? Are there any numbers?

- Ask the children to video the location and a train passing, on a tablet computer. Ask key questions 1 – 4.

Activity 2:

- Ask the children to stand in a line, looking out at the road. If there are parked cars, either move the line to a place where there is clear visibility or use your adult support to take much smaller groups to a place where they can see the road clearly.

- Record the children's responses to the following questions (or ask the children to record these):

- What are the different vehicles you can see? How do they move? How are they powered?

- Record the colours of the first 10 cars that pass by. The children could use a clicker counter or call out answers for the adult helper to record.

- Walk to a place where there are traffic lights. Ask key questions 5 – 7. Record traffic lights changing on a tablet computer.

- Look at the road markings. Point out junctions when a minor road reaches a main one; point out a box junction if there is one near a railway barrier. Point out the central lines in the road – what do they mean? Take photographs of different markings.

- Swap the groups over and complete the second half of the Trail.

KEY QUESTIONS

- 1 How does the train move and what does it move on?
- 2 What are the tracks made from?
- 3 Can you feel the vibrations as the train passes?
- 4 What sound does the train make?
- 5 What happens when the traffic lights change colour?
- 6 What is the sequence of colours when the traffic lights change?
- 7 What instructions do the children think that the traffic lights are giving road users?

BACK IN THE CLASSROOM

- The main activity will be to use the results of the survey to plot a bar chart or pictogram. The children's activities should be driven by their interests and based on their observations on the Trail, e.g. railway barriers, maps of the journey, making different-sized vehicles with construction kits, registration plates, counting wheels and ordering the numbers on houses. Children could use toy cars to model the main road they visited and complete problem-solving tasks, e.g. take away 2 cars from the road, how many wheels are there altogether?

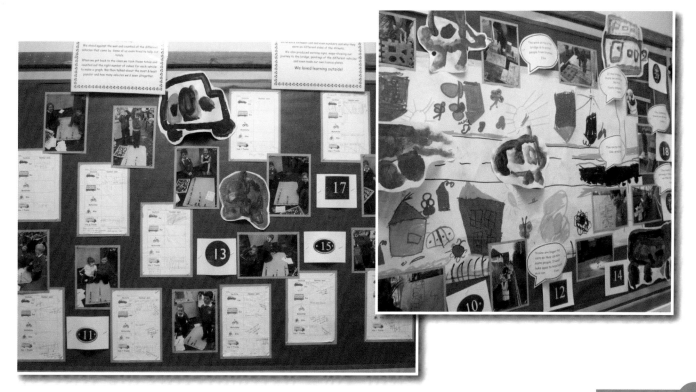

Let's Go! WOODLAND WALKING

WHICH ANIMALS LIVE IN MY LOCAL WOOD, WHERE DO THEY LIVE AND WHY?

ages 4-11

INTRODUCTION

This Trail aims to help children to identify a range of smaller habitats that exist within the wider woodland setting. They will make predictions about the type of animals that could live in the wood, based on their prior knowledge or from research about woodland creatures before going on the Trail. The children will find evidence of different creatures that live in these habitats through making observations of footprints, fur, feathers, droppings, nests, sounds, etc. They will also look at what different animals need in their habitats: the food they eat (whether they are carnivores, herbivores or omnivores), and the evidence for this. They will also consider other conditions that a habitat must provide (such as protection and a place to rear offspring). Children should be encouraged to think about whether animals build their own homes or find shelter.

KEY VOCABULARY

Ecosystem
Environment
Habitat
Food chain
Food web
Herbivore
Carnivore
Omnivore
Colony

CONCEPTS/OBJECTIVES EXPLORED

- Animals will select a habitat that provides them with everything they need for survival.
- Animals have features that make them suited to the habitat in which they live.
- Some animals are able to create their own homes whilst others cannot.
- Some animals live alone and others live in pairs, groups or colonies.

 ## LOCATION

- A wood or wooded area

 ## SCIENTIFIC SKILLS

- Observing
- Recording
- Collecting data
- Drawing conclusions based on evidence

INVESTIGATION TYPE

- Exploration
- Survey
- Classification

RESOURCES AND PREPARATION

Each group needs:

Clipboards
Paper
Pencils/pens
Digital cameras
Keys or identification charts

- Planning and trialling the Trail route you intend to take in the wood would be helpful, to ensure that you know what habitats/animals are there.
- Take photographs of clues about animals found in woods (e.g. droppings, fur, footprints, etc.) to help children identify that an animal lives in a particular place, even if they do not see the animal, e.g. mouse, owl, etc., when on the Trail.
- Some work on habitats will need to be done prior to going on the Trail, so children understand that this is where an animal or plant finds everything it needs to survive.
- Make a list of animals that the children think live in a wood.
- Do some work on how to use identification keys before going, so these can be used effectively on the Trail.

 ON THE TRAIL

WHAT TO DO

- Start by asking key question 1 and encourage the children to identify possible habitats for the animals that they have suggested. Ask key questions 2 – 4.
- Divide the children into groups and follow a circular walk that you have planned through the woods.
- Ask the children to find 5 different habitats, with or without an animal in these. Ask key question 5. (If children would like to lift a log, disturb leaf litter, etc. to record more detailed information, ensure that they have an adult with them to support this and return the item to its original position.) Reiterate key questions 3 and 4.
- In small groups, ask the children to record the following information:

    Photographs, drawings or a list of the 5 habitats that they have found

    A description of how the animal makes its home (e.g. a spider or bird) or whether it needs to find shelter (e.g. a woodlouse)

    Whether the animals are herbivores, carnivores or omnivores? Provide evidence for this

    Photographs, drawings, or a list of any evidence that an animal lives/has lived in the habitat they are observing. The children could record markings, droppings, fur, feathers, pictures of trees that have been eaten or gnawed, etc. Ask key question 6.

- Whilst in the woods, take some time to observe how the wood is managed or supported. You might like to encourage the children to find evidence of:

    Fencing: Why is it here? What is it made from? How is the structure standing?

    Bird boxes: How are they made? How do they get up into the tree? How do bird boxes support or help the birds in the woods?

    Logging: Why might woods need to have trees cut down? How have the trees been cut down? What industries might use wood or logs and why? How could logging protect or harm woods?

KEY QUESTIONS ?

- 1 Where do different animals live within the wood?
- 2 What makes you think that an animal could live there?
- 3 What are the animals' needs and how are these provided in this habitat?
- 4 What makes a 'good' home for them?
- 5 Can you find evidence of different animals, e.g. paw prints, Trails, fur, droppings, nests, sounds?
- 6 Do the animals live alone or in small or large groups or colonies?

 BACK IN THE CLASSROOM

- Children could present their findings and conclusions about the animals in the woods.
- Children could research and complete food chains/webs for animals in the woods.
- Hold a wider discussion about other wooded ecosystems or habitats and how they are affected by humans, climate change, disease, etc. (e.g. cutting down rainforests to plant palm trees for oil). How might this affect the animals that live there?
- Children could look at animals in different types of woods or forests around the world and consider similarities to and differences from local woodlands.

 **ZOO**

WHAT ANIMALS LIVE IN DIFFERENT PARTS OF THE WORLD AND HOW HAVE THEY ADAPTED TO THESE HABITATS?

 ages 4-11

INTRODUCTION

This Trail aims to encourage children to consider what kinds of animals live in places around the world, in a variety of habitats, and how they have adapted to do so. As a trip to the zoo is a fairly common activity for schools, this Trail will support teachers and children in making the most of their experience there. This is a good opportunity to look at animal adaptations in detail and compare and contrast the animals and habitats observed in the zoo with ones the children have seen in their immediate locality. Older children could also consider the ethical implications of zoos and their role in conservation of some species of animal.

CONCEPTS/OBJECTIVES EXPLORED

- Animals live around the world in a variety of habitats.
- Animals are adapted to their habitats.
- Animals can be herbivores, omnivores or carnivores.
- Animals have features that can identify them as herbivores, omnivores or carnivores.

KEY VOCABULARY

Zoo
Habitat
Indigenous
Camouflage
Invertebrate
Barren
Adaptation
Legs
Tail
Fins
Wings
Teeth
Paws
Claws
A thick coat

LOCATION

- A zoo or wildlife park

SCIENTIFIC SKILLS

- Observing
- Measuring
- Recording
- Collecting data

INVESTIGATION TYPE

- Exploration
- Survey
- Classification
- Pattern seeking

RESOURCES AND PREPARATION

■ Before the visit, children (in groups) could choose between 3 and 6 contrasting animals to observe at the zoo. The teacher could direct choices to ensure that they are diverse – choose a bird, an insect, a reptile/amphibian, a large/small mammal, a fish, an invertebrate, etc. Children could look at the zoo's webpage to make their choices of animal prior to going. They could plan the route that they intend to take, marking on the map where they are likely to see their animals. Other themes could also be selected around specific adaptations, such as by looking for herbivores, carnivores or omnivores and contrasting their teeth, claws, etc; how animals use camouflage; or, if looking at a particular place, e.g. Africa, which animals are indigenous to this continent?

Each group needs:

Digital camera
Tablet computers
Laminated cards with animal names on
Pedometers

When recording, use age appropriate methods – photographs and sound buttons/verbal recording devices/filming for younger/less confident children, the same plus written recording for older/more confident children

 ON THE TRAIL

WHAT TO DO

■ To provide an opportunity for maths/data collection, the children could all wear pedometers to measure how far they walk on their visit.

■ In groups, children should refer to the route planned on their maps and walk to the first enclosure. For key questions below, ensure that children can give evidence. Repeat activities for each enclosure/animal visited.

■ **Activity 1:** As children are likely to be very excited on approaching an enclosure, look at the animals first. Spend time just observing the animal and its adaptations. Ask questions so that children explore the animals' features, camouflage and movement/other behaviours. Ask key questions 1 and 2. Ask the children to consider if and why the animal lives with others of the same species or another species.

■ **Activity 2:** Focus on the animals' diets. Ask the children to consider what the animal eats and drinks. Is it a carnivore, herbivore or omnivore? Discuss the features that give clues about the animals' diets. Consider how the feeding regime compares to natural behaviours (and natural predator/prey relationships). Ask key question 3.

■ **Activity 3:** Focus on the habitat and ask the children to describe the features and whether these are natural or artificial to simulate a natural environment. Ensure that the children relate the features of the habitat to the animal that lives there (e.g. monkeys might be provided with ropes on which to swing/climb). Ask the children to consider and record the features that enable the animal to live there successfully.

■ **Activity 4:** Focus on the enclosure. Discuss its size compared to that of the animal. What materials have been used to make the enclosure strong and safe and ensure that the animals can still be seen? Take photographs of the enclosure. Ask key questions 5 and 6.

■ Record or photograph any additional information about the animal, e.g. where it is indigenous, or any facts that children find interesting.

KEY QUESTIONS

- 1 Does the animal have legs, a tail, fins, paws, claws, a thick coat?
- 2 What colour, pattern, or markings does the animal have?
- 3 How is water provided for the animal?
- 4 What trees, plants, rocks or other natural things can be seen?
- 5 Is the enclosure, tank or cage heated in some way?
- 6 What shapes have been used to construct the cages/structures etc?

 ## BACK IN THE CLASSROOM

- Use evidence that children have recorded about different animals, their habitats and adaptations to compare with animals found locally. What invertebrates, mammals, birds, amphibians or reptiles live near them? What are their similarities and differences?

- Discuss how the enclosures or cages were constructed. Could the children construct hides and dens, or make their own enclosures at school?

- For older children, look into ethical debates about zoos and their purpose. How do they help with conservation? How is the welfare of the animals ensured?

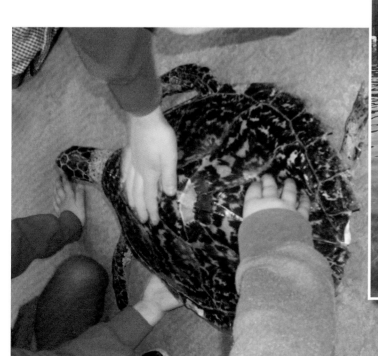

GLOSSARY

This glossary is not designed to be a textbook definition of the words it contains; rather we hope that this section will help teachers and children alike to understand these words better by providing examples of use, as well as descriptions of their meaning as appropriate. If you have good definitions, please share them with us and we will add them to the on-line glossary.

BIOLOGY

adaptation	Where an animal or plant becomes better suited to its environment through a process of physical changes. For example, polar bears have adapted to be white in colour and have a thick layer of fat under their skin to ensure that they can survive and blend in with the extreme environment of the Arctic.
adolescent	A post-pubescent young person in the process of developing from an child to a adult.
adult	A living organism that has been through the process of adolescence and has fully grown and developed.
animals	A living organism. Animals will be able to sense and respond to the world around them, are able to grow, move and reproduce, respire and excrete.
antennae	Usually come in pairs and are used by a variety of animals to sense their surroundings. Insects and crustaceans have antennae, but snails and slugs do not, they have tentacles.
anther	An oval-shaped structure that produces the pollen. The anther Is found at the end of the filament and both comprise the male reproductive part of the flower called the stamen.
antibacterial	A material or substance that stops or prevents bacteria from growing.
antiseptic	A material or substance that stops or prevents microorganisms from growing.
autumn	A season. In the northern hemisphere, autumn starts in September and includes the months October and November.
baby	A very young child.
beak	A hard projecting mouth structure.
bee	A flying insect that is an important global pollinator, collecting pollen and nectar. They live in colonies (large communities) where there is one queen, and produce honey and wax.
behaviour	How a person or animal responds to a situation or stimulus.
bird	An animal that is warm-blooded and egg-laying. It also has an internal skeleton (a vertebrate) and has the physical features of feathers, wings, a beak. Most, but not all, birds can fly.
breathing	Taking air into the lungs and then expelling it.
bug	Another word for a small insect or a harmful microorganism that can cause illness.
butterfly	An adult caterpillar. It is an insect that feeds on nectar and so helps to pollinate flowers. It has brightly-coloured wings that are covered with tiny scales.
carbohydrate	Sugars, starch and cellulose are all carbohydrates. Once ingested, a sugar can be broken down by an animal to release energy, sometimes rapidly.

cardiovascular system	A system is comprised of the heart, blood, blood vessels and lungs in vertebrates. Another word for it is circulatory system. The lymphatic system is also considered to be a part of the cardiovascular system. It is responsible for moving (transporting) nutrients (found in food) around the body to where they are needed, as well as oxygen (taken in as air in the lungs). It is also responsible for transporting waste products to organs to get rid of them (excretion).
carpel	The female part of a flower. There are three main parts to the carpel: the stigma, style and ovary. This is where the fruit is made.
child	A young person typically between the ages of one year and puberty.
circulation	The movement of a fluid around a closed system, for example, blood around arteries, veins and capillaries.
classification	A way of organising living things into similar groups sharing similar features or properties.
claws	Nails at the end of an animal's digits (toes), which are particularly sharp.
daylight	The time between sunrise (dawn) and sunset (dusk).
dependence	Being reliant on something.
dispersal	The process by which a plant spreads its seeds, so the new plants are not in competition with the parent plants when they start to grow. A plant is either adapted to use the wind (dandelion seeds), water (coconut), force (poppy seeds), or animals (blackberry seeds) to disperse its seeds.
diurnal	Referring to animals, diurnal animals are active during the day and sleep at night.
diversity	The range of things that can be observed.
Easter	A Christian festival celebrating the resurrection of Christ. It usually occurs in spring. Easter also depicts new life and new growth.
elderly	Someone in the later stages of life. Someone who is old or visibly ageing.
exercise	An activity to improve a person's level of fitness and to maintain their health. Exercise should take some effort and raise the heart rate.
fat	An energy source and essential to the body. Humans cannot survive without it and it is essential for making things called hormones. It also helps the body absorb and process vitamins A, D, E and K.
feather	For birds, feathers are epidermal growths and form part of a bird's outer covering. Feathers can be a variety of colours.
fertilisation	The fusion of male and female gametes to form a zygote.
filament	The long tube attached to the anther. Forms part of the stamen.
flower	The reproductive part of a plant. Flowers can have sepals, petals, stigma and stamen. Once fertilised, the flower usually becomes the fruit, nut or seeds.
flowering plant	A living organism producing flowers, fruit, seeds and nuts. The scientific word for them is angiosperms. It makes its own food through the process of photosynthesis (which takes place in green parts of the plant, mainly the leaves).
fly	A flying insect. It lays eggs and its larvae are without wings. The scientific word for it is *Diptera*, which comes from the Greek word *Di* – meaning two and *ptera* – meaning wings. This is a huge group of insects with an estimated 1,000,000 species. Mosquitoes, flies, midges and crane flies are all part of this group.
food	Used to give living things energy so that they can do a variety of things such as move and grow. Food is also made into new material by living things, such as new body tissue or repairing parts of the body. Food consists of nutrients such as fats, proteins, carbohydrates, vitamins and minerals.
food groups	How we group similar foods that share similar characteristics or do similar things in the body.
fruit	Made after fertilisation has happened. It is the part of a plant or tree that can be eaten, can contain seeds and is usually quite fleshy.

function	What something does – its job. The reason why it is there.
germination	When a seed begins to sprout and grow.
growth	The irreversible increase in how big (mass) an organism gets. It cannot be changed back.
habitat	The environment in which an organism resides.
harvest	Harvest is a time to gather ripe crops from the fields and store them. It is a time of plenty, making provisions for the winter months ahead where there is much less growth, thus marking the end of the main growing season. A festival celebrating the produce grown in the summer months.
health	The condition of body and mind (physical and mental health).
healthy lifestyle	For optimum health, a human needs to eat a balanced diet, be active and take regular exercise.
heart	A pump in vertebrates (animals with a backbone) that is responsible for moving blood around the body and to and from the lungs.
hibernate	When an animal goes to sleep for the winter months. Typically an animal will feed and build up fat reserves prior to hibernation.
humans	A species of animal known as *homo sapiens*.
insect	A small animal that has six legs, three body parts and usually one or two pairs of wings. Also known as arthropods' (Otherwise this implies that the wings are arthropods!)
interdependence	Inter means between, so this is how living things depend on each other. For example, the plants and animals in a habitat or ecosystem. A bird relies on a blackberry plant to live and the blackberry plant relies on the bird to disperse its seeds.
invertebrate	An animal that does not have a backbone. Insects, molluscs, crustaceans and arachnids (spiders) are all invertebrates. About 95% of animals are invertebrates, so they make up a huge part of the animal kingdom.
life cycle	The process of life from creation of a zygote (a fertilised egg) to death. How a living thing grows, develops and then declines and dies.
microorganism	A living thing (organism) that can only be seen with a microscope because it is so small.
mineral	Important for healthy bones, teeth, blood, skin and hair. They also help muscles and nerves function properly.
minibeast	Another name for a small invertebrate animal such as an insect (bee), mollusc (slug) or arachnid (spider).
mollusc (slug, snail)	An invertebrate animal. They have a long soft body that is in one piece (not segmented or in parts). If they have a shell it is mostly or partly made from a material called calcium carbonate (calcareous) containing chalk or lime.
nectar	Another way that flowers attract insects and animals to help pollinate them. It is a sugary liquid secreted (made and released) inside the flower. Bees make honey from nectar.
nocturnal	Being active during the night and sleeping in the day.
nose	A sensory organ that has receptors that respond to certain chemicals; this response causes a signal to be sent to the brain that is then processed and assigned a smell.
nutrition	The study of food and how it works in the body, or how the body uses it. Eating the correct foods and food groups is essential for growth and development.
organism	Something that is alive. A living thing.
ovary	A part of the female reproductive organ where unfertilised eggs are stored.
petal	A typically brightly coloured part of a flower that surrounds reproductive organs.
physical features	In the context of living thing, the features that make it part of a species or group. The things you can see about a living thing's appearance such as ears or eyes, or, for plants, things like their structure – stem, leaves and flowers.

plant	A living organism. It makes its own food through the process of photosynthesis.
pollen	This is a microscopic (very small) part of a flower that contains the male reproductive material. Fertilisation cannot happen without it.
pollination	The process in which pollen (male cell) is transferred to the female reproductive organs so that fertilisation and reproduction can take place in plants.
protein	Essential to the body for growth and repair.
pulse rate	A measurement of the number of heartbeats in a given time.
qualitative	Collecting data that is observed, not measured in any way. Describing something, for example, colours, smells, tastes, physical appearance, or a case study.
quantitative	Requiring the measurement of a variable or variables.
refrigeration	The process of removing heat from a container to keep the contents inside cool.
reproduction	The process by which organisms produce new living organisms with characteristics or features similar to those of the parents.
respiration	A chemical process that generates energy in living things.
season	A year is divided into four seasons. They can be recognised by changes in the weather, number of hours in the day and the changes to the environment and ecology that occur.
seed	A potential new plant covered in a protective outer coating.
sepal	Protects the flower when it is a bud. They form a protective layer over the petals.
sight	One of the five senses. The ability to see objects using eyes.
smell	One of the five senses. The ability to sense the odour or scent of something.
spring	A season. In the northern hemisphere, spring starts in March and includes the months of April and May.
stamen	The male part of the plant consisting of a filament and anther.
stigma	Part of the female reproductive organs of a plant, where pollination occurs.
structure	How something is arranged, built or organised.
structure of a plant	The parts of a plant are the stem, leaves, roots, and flowers and they are organised or fit together to work for the benefit of the plant.
style	Part of the female reproductive organs of a plant. This connects the stigma to the ovary in a flowering plant.
summer	A season. In the northern hemisphere, summer starts in June and includes the months of July and August.
survival	To continue to live or exist even in challenging circumstances. Survival can relate to an individual or a species.
taste	One of the five senses. When a chemical lands on the tongue it triggers a response (in the taste buds) and this is converted into a signal that is transported to the brain and interpreted.
teenager	A human between the ages of 13 and 19.
temperature	The scale of how hot or cold something is. There are a number of temperature scales, such as the Celsius scale, where zero is defined as the freezing point of water and 100 the boiling point.
toddler	A human child who has started to walk independently (loosely defined as up to the age of 3 years).
tongue	An organ in the mouth that has taste buds on it.
touch	One of the five senses. The ability to be able to feel things through the skin by the process of signals passing between the skin and the brain.
vitamin	Chemicals that are essential for life, in particular growth and repair.

wasp	A flying insect. It has black and yellow stripes and can sting. Wasps can pollinate flowers. They live in nests with other wasps.
webbed feet	Where the toes on the feet are connected by skin. Webbed feet help water birds, for example, ducks, to swim better.
wings	A part of a bird or insect that is used for flight. Usually wings come in pairs, or sets of pairs, for example, 2 or 4.
winter	A season. In the northern hemisphere, winter starts in December and includes the months of January and February. It is usually the coldest season of all four, with plants becoming dormant and some animals hibernating.
woodlouse	A small animal that has seven pairs of legs and a grey body. Its body is made up of segments and it usually likes living in damp habitats, such as under fallen logs or in woodland. The scientific word is crustacean, so it is in the same group of animals as crabs.

CHEMISTRY

alive	See living
asbestos	A naturally occurring silicate mineral that has been used in construction.
atmosphere	The gaseous envelope that surrounds some, but not all, planets. In our solar system, Mercury does not have an atmosphere. Our Moon also does not have an atmosphere. Earth's atmosphere is mainly nitrogen (78%) and oxygen (21%).
brick	A brick was originally made from clay and is used in a variety of buildings and structures.
building	Typically, a building is considered to be a construction that has a roof and walls. It may be permanent but may also be a temporary structure (e.g. at the Olympic Park in London in 2012).
chalk	A form of a compound called calcium carbonate ($CaCO_3$). Other examples of this compound include marble.
clay	A naturally occurring soil that contains metal oxides and organic material. It becomes hard and brittle when it dries out.
cloud	Comprised of many tiny droplets of liquid water that reflect and absorb visible light.
concrete	Usually a lime-based material used in construction that can be 'poured' but will harden over time.
condensation	When a gas is cooled down, the gas particles become closer together. If the gas is cooled sufficiently, the particles begin to stick together (or coalesce) to form a liquid; at this point condensation is taking place.
Cretaceous	A period in Earth's history that extended from 145.5 million years ago to 65.5 million years ago and marks the end of the period known as the Mesozoic Era. Also the point at which the dinosaurs became extinct.
dead	An organism that was alive and has ceased to live.
discolouration	The process of changing to a different colour (often an unfavourable one).
drainage	When water is removed from a surface, naturally or by human intervention, drainage is taking place.
drop/droplet	A small body of liquid that is separated from the main body of liquid.
durability	The durability of an object is its ability to withstand wear and erosion.
evaporation	When a liquid is heated up, the particles in the liquid gain energy and move further apart. Eventually, if enough energy is added, the particles in the liquid can escape from the bulk liquid and become a gas; at this point evaporation is taking place.
evolution	Change in the heritable traits of biological populations over successive generations.

felt	A textile that can be made from natural (e.g. wool) or synthetic fibres (acrylic).
flash flood	During heavy rainfall, a system may become overwhelmed by the volume of water and flood rapidly.
flint	A sedimentary rock made of quartz, typically quite hard.
flood	When an area of land that is normally dry is submerged by water, it is said to have flooded.
flood defence	Structures that are built to either increase the height of existing structures to prevent flood breaches or to divert flowing water away from a flood risk area, thus reducing the risk of flooding.
fossil	The preserved remains or traces of animals, plants and other organisms from the remote past.
gas	In a gas, the particles that make up the gas are very far apart; the gas will flow and will not support its own shape, but will tend to fill a space into which it can flow.
geology	In general terms the study of rocks, how they are made and how they will be transformed.
glass	Glass, as used in windows, is a non-crystalline solid.
gravel	A collection of small stones.
hail	Ice pellets that are made through the rapid freezing of rain drops.
hard	A material may be described as hard or soft and this is a relative term that reflects the ability of the material to resist deformation, e.g. compression.
igneous	An igneous rock is made when magma or lava (from volcanoes) cools.
impermeable	A material is impermeable to a fluid if it prevents that fluid from passing through it.
insulation	When an object is insulated, the insulation is typically designed to keep energy within the system (e.g. heat or sound) and prevent it from escaping.
Jurassic	A period in Earth's history that extended from 201.3 million years ago to 145.5 million years ago.
limestone	Limestone, like chalk, is made of calcium carbonate and is a sedimentary rock.
liquid	In a liquid, the particles that make up the liquid are further apart than in a solid; the liquid can flow and will take the shape of its container.
magnetism	The force caused by magnets that can attract or repel certain objects in an area around the magnet called the magnetic field. When an electric charge moves, it causes a magnetic field to be generated.
material	The substance (matter) from which an object is made.
metal	Typically a solid that conducts heat and electricity very well and is therefore a good conductor.
metamorphic	Metamorphic rocks are made when other rock types are exposed to high temperatures and/or high pressures.
mudstone	A sedimentary rock made from consolidated mud.
opaque	A material that is opaque absorbs or reflects light that falls on it and does not allow the light to pass right through.
pavement	A stone structure used for surfaces to be used by pedestrians.
permeable	A material is permeable to a fluid if it allows that fluid to pass through it.
plastic	A polymer that may have natural or synthetic origins.
porous	An object that is porous will typically contain a lot of pores, holes or small spaces that allow a fluid (gas or liquid) to pass through it.
precipitation	When water is released from a cloud, it may be in the form of rain, hail, sleet, snow or even freezing rain; all are forms of precipitation.
prehistoric	Prehistoric or prehistory refers to a time before history was recorded by humans.
rain	The liquid water form of precipitation.
rainbow	When light is reflected, refracted and dispersed by water droplets, a rainbow is formed.
rock	A naturally occurring solid that may contain a number of minerals.

roof	The covering on the uppermost part of a building construction.
rough	A surface may be described as rough or smooth and this is a measure of the degree of friction that it displays.
run off	When excess water accumulates and flows over a land mass and beyond.
saturation	When a material cannot absorb any more of a particular substance.
sedimentary	Sedimentary rocks are formed when solid material is compacted together.
shower	Rain for a short duration.
signs of a living thing	Movement, reproduction, respiration (breathing), sensitivity to the environment (e.g. light, finding shelter), nutrition (eating), growth, excretion (breathing out, urination).
slate	A metamorphic rock that was made from sedimentary rock (shale-like).
snow	Precipitation in the form of flakes of crystalline water ice.
solid	In a solid, the particles that make up the solid are close together; the solid will not flow and will support its own shape.
soluble	When a material (solid or liquid) dissolves in a particular liquid, the material is soluble.
stone	A hard solid made of non-metallic mineral matter.
storm	Any disturbed state of an environment or astronomical body's atmosphere especially affecting its surface, and strongly implying severe weather.
straw	When a stalk of grain is dried, it is straw.
tiles	Thin rectangular slabs of baked clay or other material, used in overlapping rows for covering roofs.
translucent	A material is translucent if light can pass through it, but no detailed shapes can be determined when looking through it.
transparent	A material that allows light to pass through is said to be transparent.
tsunami	After an earthquake, it is possible for the sea floor to be raised slightly over the affected area. This also raises the sea above the affected area. Now there is a volume of water that is above the surrounding sea and it will flow out across the sea until the level equilibrates or it reaches land. This wave of water is called a tsunami and can travel thousands of miles across an ocean.
water	Dihyrogen monoxide or H_2O, it freezes at zero degrees celsius and boils at one hundred degrees celsius.
water cycle	When heated by the Sun, the ocean's liquid water evaporates and becomes a gas (water vapour). This water vapour may rise in altitude (height) from the ocean surface because it has gained energy in a process called convection. As the water vapour rises in altitude it will cool down (in effect using up its excess energy) and can condense to form clouds. Eventually, the cloud may become saturated with water and rain will occur. The rain or liquid water can then fall back to the surface of the Earth, either to the ocean or the land. If on land, it may then be transported to a river, which eventually transports it back to the ocean. Hence we have established a water cycle.
water purification	Water can become polluted with a range of materials, living (e.g. bacteria) and non-living (e.g. dissolved solids or liquids). In order to be able to drink that water safely, it needs to be purified, i.e. these pollutants need to be removed. There are many ways to purify water, depending on the pollutant, e.g. boiling liquid water and collecting the water vapour formed, or passing the water through a solid filter to remove suspended particles (there are many others).
water vapour	Gaseous form of water.
waterproof	A material that is coated in a substance that does not allow water to pass through.
weathering	When a material is eroded by wind, rain, sand, water flowing, etc., it is said to be undergoing weathering (i.e. a natural process).
wood	A hard fibrous material.

PHYSICS

absorption	To absorb means to incorporate into the object. An object can absorb energy or other entities such as water.
accelerate	When an object increases its speed it is said to be accelerating. If the increase in speed is the same over each time segment, the acceleration is constant or uniform.
air resistance	When an object moves through the atmosphere, it will move past air molecules, which will resist the movement through friction. This is known as air resistance.
balanced	When two opposing forces are equal they are balanced; when equal masses are compared on a scale they are balanced; therefore one definition of when a system is balanced is that the forces acting on that system are equal and opposite.
battery	A chemical source of energy.
colour	Our eyes can respond to light in the so-called visible spectrum. Light can be thought of as a wave and different wavelengths produce different colours. Visible light has an associated wavelength between approximately 400nm (violet) and 700nm (red). The energy per photon of light is greater for violet light than red light.
dark	Not a defined term but indicates the absence of light; when no light is present the term total darkness may be used.
day	Defined as the time taken for the Earth to complete one revolution about its axis, which is approximately 24 hours (slightly less). On other planets in our solar system, a day is very different. For Jupiter it is just 10 hours, but for Venus it is 5,832 hours.
decelerate	When an object decreases in speed it is said to be decelerating. If the decrease in speed is the same over each time segment, the deceleration is constant or uniform.
distance	The displacement between two objects. The SI (international system of units or Système international d'unités) unit of distance is the metre.
ears	Sensory organs used to receive sound waves and convert these to a signal that can be interpreted by the brain.
Earth	The third planet in our solar system from the Sun, and the only known planet in the universe to host living organisms.
electrical appliance	Any device that requires electrical energy to operate.
electricity	When there is a flow of electrons around a circuit, electricity is generated.
energy	The ability to do work. There are many forms of energy, including: heat, sound, electrical, light and movement (kinetic). A system will have a certain amount of energy distributed amongst the various forms.
eyes	These are sensory organs used to receive light waves and convert this to a signal that can be interpreted by the brain.
force	A force is a push or pull upon an object resulting from the object's interaction with another object.
frequency	The frequency of a wave is the number of waves that pass a certain point each second. The unit of frequency is the hertz (Hz) but can also be expressed as per second.
friction	A force that resists motion. When two objects move past each other, there is a friction force that slows their motion.
fulcrum	The pivotal point about which a lever operates.
gnomon	On a sundial, that element that projects upwards and can causes a shadow, thus allowing the time to be determined by the position of that shadow.

gravity	Gravity is a force between two objects based on their mass and the distance between them. Typically we think of gravity acting between an object and the Earth, where the acceleration due to gravity is 9.8 m/s^2.
heat	Heat is a form of energy. Heat energy always flows from a warmer to a colder place.
human-made	An object made by humans and NOT occurring naturally.
inertia	The reluctance of an object at rest to move, and the tendency of an object to resist acceleration.
intermittent	A signal can be continuous, e.g. a bell ringing continuously; or it can ring and then stop, ring and then stop, which would be an example of intermittent behaviour.
kilowatt hour	The consumption of one thousand watts in one hour.
lever	A simple machine consisting of a rigid bar resting on a pivot or fulcrum.
light	Light here refers to visible light. Light travels in straight lines and can pass through a vacuum, compared with sound, which cannot. Violet light is the most energetic, i.e. carries the most energy per photon (particle of light), through to red light, which carries the least energy per photon.
light source	An object that generates light, such as the Sun, but other examples include a torch.
living	The definition of living is controversial and constantly under debate. However, as a working definition, for an organism to be alive it would need to grow, adapt to its environment, respond to stimuli, excrete and reproduce.
load	Typically refers to a mass added to an object.
loud	Typically refers to the amplitude of a sound wave. Louder sounds have more energy than quieter ones.
lumens	The total amount of visible light from a light source is measured in lumens.
mains powered	Any device that requires electrical energy from the mains supply (not a battery) to operate.
mass	The amount of matter in an object. The standard unit of mass is the kilogramme (kg).
night	Typically night is defined as starting at sunset and ending at sunrise and is typified by a lack of daylight.
non-living	A system that does not display the characteristics of a living organism (see living)
opaque	A material that is opaque absorbs or reflects light that falls on it and does not allow the light to pass right through.
pitch	How high or low a note is, referring to the frequency of the sound produced by an object.
pull	A way to describe a force that is stretching an object.
push	A way to describe a force that is compressing or squashing an object.
reflection	The change in direction of a light ray away from a surface instead of passing through it. When light hits a reflective or shiny surface, it will reflect from and travel away from the surface in a predictable path. Snell's Law indicates that the angle of incidence (the angle that the light beam makes with the surface) is equal to the angle of reflection.
rotation	When an object undergoes circular motion.
senses	Senses allow an organism to explore the environment it is in, through sight, hearing, touch, taste and smell.
shadow	When an object blocks the path of light, preventing the light from passing through, a shadow forms. The shadow is an area of less light than the surroundings, or a complete absence of light. Shadows appears behind the object, on the opposite side to the light source.
slow down	See decelerate.

soft	Referring to solid materials, their softness is a relative scale. If we apply a force to a series of solids, we can determine the order of softness by observing the force required to bend the solid, for example. The less force required, the softer the object; the one requiring the least force to be bent would be the softest.
sound	A form of energy created by vibrations that can be transferred from one particle to the next. Sound travels best through solids where particles are closest together, next through liquids and worst through gases, where particles are furthest apart. Sound cannot travel in a vacuum (absence of any particles).
sound source	In order to generate a sound, something needs to vibrate (see vibration) and so a sound source will be a device that creates vibrations.
sound wave	Sound travels as a wave known as a longitudinal wave. The frequency of the wave (number of waves arriving per second) determines the type of sound (high pitch for high frequency and low pitch for low frequency) and the amplitude of the wave determines how loud the sound is: the larger the amplitude the larger the sound.
squash	A term used when an object is being compressed, i.e. forces are being applied.
stretch	If an object is pulled (force) in two different directions at the same time, it will be stretched.
Sun	A star and is 93 million miles away from the Earth.
translucence	When a material lets light through, but it is not possible to observe any material clearly within the object, the object is said to be translucent. Windows used in bathrooms are often translucent; they let light in and out but it is not possible to see a defined image inside the bathroom.
transparent	If a material allows light to enter and exit so that it is possible to observe an object in or behind that material, the material is said to be transparent.
twist	A force that is a combination of a push and a pull. Turning something repeatedly would be an example of a twist.
unbalanced	Referring to balance, when forces acting on a system are not equal and opposite, a system is unbalanced; when unequal masses are added to a set of weighing scales they will tip down towards the larger mass.
upthrust	Where an object is wholly or partially immersed in a fluid (gas or usually a liquid), there is a force upwards on the object known as upthrust – this is equal to the weight of the fluid displaced (Archimedes Principle). The buoyancy force is an example of upthrust.
vibration	A repeated movement either side of a fixed point, e.g. side to side or up and down.
vision	The ability to see an object. If someone has long vision (or long sight) they can see faraway objects well, but see a blurred image for objects nearby. Short vision (or short sight) is the opposite.
volume	The amount of 3-dimensional space that an object occupies. The volume of a cube or cuboid is found by multiplying together its length by its width by its height.
water resistance	When an object moves through water it has to move the water molecules out of the way and this causes a resistance to movement, known as water resistance.
weight	The force of gravity on an object, calculated by multiplying its mass by the acceleration due to gravity. Weight is measured in Newtons (N).

MATHS

digit	Single symbols used to make numerals.
dimension	A measurable extent (size). In maths, the minimum number of coordinates needed to specify a point within a shape.
number	A mathematical means of counting, measuring or labelling.
numeral	The symbol used to represent a number.
shape	Any area or volume enclosed by a line or surface. Geometric shapes may be regular, such as a square or circle, or irregular (where angles and side lengths differ).

2-DIMENSIONAL (2D) SHAPES:

circle	1 side. Radius is the distance from the centre of circle to its edge. Diameter is the distance across the circle through the centrepoint (twice the radius in length). Circumference is the distance around the edge of the circle.
triangle	3 sides. sum of internal angles is 180°; an equilateral triangle: all sides equal length and all angles equal (60°); right angled triangle has one angle of 90°; an isosceles triangle has 2 sides equal length and 2 equal angles; a scalene triangle has no sides or angles equal.

QUADRILATERALS: 4-sided shapes.

square	4 sides of equal length; opposite sides are parallel; four right angles.
rectangle	4 sides – opposite pairs of equal length; four right angles. (A square is a rectangle with all sides of equal length).
rhombus	4 sides of equal length; opposite sides parallel; opposite angles equal.
parallelogram	2 pairs of sides of equal length; opposite sides parallel; opposite angles equal.
trapezium	1 pair of sides of equal length.
kite	No parallel sides. Pairs of adjacent sides are equal in length.

POLYGONS: 2-dimensional shapes that enclose an area with a number of straight sides.

pentagon	5 sides. Regular pentagon: sides of equal length and all internal angles equal. Irregular pentagon: any 5-sided shape where at least 2 sides are of different length.
hexagon	6 sides. Regular hexagon: sides of equal length and all internal angles equal. Irregular hexagon: any 6-sided shape where at least 2 sides are of different length.
heptagon	7 sides. Regular heptagon: sides of equal length and all internal angles equal. Irregular heptagon: any 7-sided shape where at least 2 sides are of different length.
octagon	8 sides. Regular octagon: sides of equal length and all internal angles equal. Irregular octagon: any 8-sided shape where at least 2 sides are of different length.
nonagon	9 sides. Regular nonagon: sides of equal length and all internal angles equal. Irregular nonagon: any 9-sided shape where at least 2 sides are of different length.
decagon	10 sides. Regular decagon: sides of equal length and all internal angles equal. Irregular decagon: any 10-sided shape where at least 2 sides are of different length.
perimeter	The distance around the outside of any 2D shape. Measurement units of length (mm, cm, m, km...)
area	The total surface covered by a 2D shape. Measurement units of length squared (mm^2, cm^2, m^2, km^2...)

3-DIMENSIONAL (3D) SHAPES: Any shape with length, width and depth, enclosing a volume of space within it.

volume	A measure of the space enclosed by any 3-dimensional object. Measurement units of length cubed (mm^3, cm^3, m^3, km^3...)

sphere	A round solid with one surface where every point on the surface is an equal distance from a central point.
prism	Any 3D shape with a constant cross-section. Ends are the same shape and a slice parallel to the ends will reveal this same shape.
cube	A 6-sided shape where each face is a square and is at 90° to each adjoining surface.
cuboid	A 6-sided shape where each face is a rectangle and is at 90° to each adjoining surface.
cylinder	A prism with 2 faces that are circular.
triangular prism	A prism with 2 faces that are triangular.
hexagonal prism	A prism with 2 faces that are hexagonal.
cone	A (usually) circular-based 3D shape that tapers to a point. Slicing the shape at any level parallel to the base will reveal a cross-section the same shape as the base but of varying dimensions (increasingly smaller from base to apex).
triangular-based pyramid	A 4-sided 3D shape where all sides are triangular and sloping sides meet at a point.
square-based pyramid	A 5-sided 3D shape with a square base and 4 triangular sloping sides that meet at a point.
net	A 2-dimensional shape that when folded will create a 3-dimensional shape.
SYMMETRY:	When an object becomes exactly the same as another when it is moved in some way — by flipping or turning.
line, mirror or reflection symmetry	Two objects can only be symmetrical if they are the same shape and size but one is in a different position to the other. An object may display symmetry within it if it is possible to draw a line across the object where one side is the mirror image of the other. This is known as line, mirror or reflection symmetry. There may be more than one line of symmetry in an object.
rotational symmetry	Rotational symmetry exists when an object is rotated around a central point (centre of rotation) and at some point during the rotation looks exactly as it did before rotation. The order of rotational symmetry indicates the number of positions during rotation when the object displays symmetry. Order 1 means no rotational symmetry. Order 2 indicates that the object displays symmetry when turned through 180°. Order 3 indicates the object displays symmetry when turned through 120°, etc.
congruent shapes	Shapes are congruent if they have identical shape and size (but are not necessarily orientated in the same way).
tessellation	A repeating pattern (of tiles) where the same shape is used over and over again with no gaps or overlaps in the pattern.
translation	A function that moves a shape from one position to another without rotation or reflection or change of size.
ANGLE:	an angle is formed where 2 lines come together at a point. This point is also called a vertex.
acute angle	An angle that is less than 90° in size.
obtuse angle	An angle that is greater than 90° and less than 180° in size.
reflex angle	An angle that is greater than 180° and less than 360° in size.
right angle	An angle of 90°.
perpendicular lines	Lines at right angles (90°) to each other.
parallel lines	Lines that have a constant distance between them.

ENGINEERING & TECHNOLOGY

algorithm	A set of rules (operations) that are to be followed, exactly as defined, to solve a problem (especially by a computer).
axle	A rod that passes through the centre of a wheel, or wheels, to enable it to spin or to fix it in place.
automaton	A moving mechanical device (machine) that performs an instructed function. Automatons may imitate the movements of a human being.
balance	When force is distributed to enable an object to remain stationary, i.e. when forces on an object are equal in opposite directions around any potential pivot point.
blueprint	The design or plan for an object, usually represented as a technical drawing.
cog	The tooth at the edge of a gear wheel or bar that will link into another gear as they turn together.
computer code	The instructions of a computer programme.
computer programme	A series of lines of computer code that, when followed, achieve a specific outcome – this 'tells' the computer what to do.
construction	The action or process of building something.
design	A plan or drawing that shows the intended look and function of an object before it is made.
energy	The ability to do work. There are many forms of energy, including: heat, sound, electrical, light and movement (kinetic). A system will have a certain amount of energy distributed amongst the various forms.
engine	A machine that creates motion (force) from input energy, such as heat from burning a fuel, or electricity.
engineering	The application of science and mathematics to solve practical problems and to design and make machines and structures.
fabric	Often the term is used to mean any flexible material made from a network of fibres (cloth). The term is also used to refer to the structure of a building.
fabrication	The process of manufacturing (making) something.
fluid	Any substance that is able to flow or take the shape of its container. Liquids and gases are fluids.
force	A push or pull upon an object resulting from the object's interaction with another object.
fulcrum	The pivot around which a lever turns; the point at which something that is balancing is supported.
gear	A toothed wheel that works with another to alter the action of a force (changing its direction or speed of movement).
generate	Produce or create.
hoist	The means of lifting something using ropes and pulley.

lever	A simple machine consisting of a rigid bar that rests on a pivot. When a force (effort) is applied to the pivot, it moves an object (load). Levers are often used to reduce the effort needed to move the load.
load	Typically refers to a mass added to an object.
machine	Any device with moving parts that work together to perform a task.
manufacture	Make something, generally using machinery.
mass	The amount of matter in an object. The standard unit of mass is the kilogramme (kg).
motor	A device that is powered by electricity or internal combustion to create motion. An electric motor converts electrical energy into mechanical (kinetic or potential) energy.
pivot	The point at which an object rotates.
power	The rate of production of energy.
production	The act of making or manufacturing something.
propulsion	A force that pushes something forwards.
pulley	A wheel with a grooved rim. By passing a cord or chain around this rim, a pulley can be used to change the direction of an applied force to move an object.
revolution	The turning around or rotating about an axis to complete one full cycle (mechanics); the movement of one object around another to complete a full orbit (astronomy).
rotation	Turning around an axis.
shape	The form of or external boundary or surface of an object.
solar	Relating to the Sun.
stability	The ability of an object to resist applied forces, especially those that would produce undesirable movement.
strength	The ability of a material to withstand an applied load without failing.
structure	A series of connected and interrelated parts that can hold an applied load (including its own weight) and remain rigid.
technology	The method by which scientific knowledge is used for a practical purpose. This term often refers to the most up-to-date and efficient means of accomplishing a task.
tool	A device that is designed to carry out a particular function. Often, tools are held in the hand (e.g. hammer, screwdriver, saw), but this is not always the case.
vacuum	A space where there is no matter.
valve	A mechanism that controls flow of fluids by opening and closing. Valves may be used to ensure that flow occurs in one direction only.
vibration	Back-and-forth motion of particles around a point.
weight	The force of gravity on an object, calculated by multiplying its mass by the acceleration due to gravity. Weight is measured in Newtons (N).
weld	A joint between pieces of metal (or plastics) created by heating the edges so that these melt and then cool to fuse together.